Science 2

Elaine Chantler

Acknowledgements

I would like to offer my grateful thanks to the headteacher Anne Siggins and the staff and pupils of Priory Fields Primary School, Dover, in particular to Ruth Bishop, Lisa Vick, Shara Wheeler, Sarah Harris, Debbie Wilshaw, Ali Poole and Debbie Bailey for their valuable assistance with creating displays for this book.

My thanks also go to Wendy Whitman, Chris Martin, the Fry family, the Mackintosh family, Chris Thomas (artist-in-residence for the Bien-Etre project), Zoë Parish and Steve Forest.

I would like to dedicate this book to my wonderful mum Margaret.

From Grouping and Changing Materials on page 42

Commissioning Editor: Zoë Parish   Editor: Melody Ismail   Cover Design: Sophie Pelham
Page Layout: Martin Cross   Photography: Steve Forest   Illustrations: Ruth Murray

First Published in 2008 by Belair Publications.

Every effort has been made to trace the copyright holders of material used in this publication. If any copyright holder has been overlooked, we should be pleased to make the necessary arrangements.

British Library Cataloguing in the Publication Data. A catalogue record for this publication is available from the British Library.

ISBN 978-1-84191-462-6

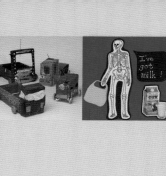

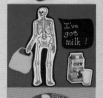

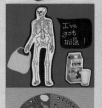

Contents

These grids demonstrate the learning objectives covered in the activities within the theme. The curriculum references indicate the relevant programme of study (PoS) for a subject area unless otherwise stated.

	Learning Objectives	Curriculum References
Science (Page 6)		
Scientific Enquiry	Plan and conduct investigations about force and movement, predicting possible outcomes. Make and record observations. Communicate findings, explaining and comparing results. Use knowledge and understanding to draw and explain conclusions.	Sc1/2a-j
	Use a digital camera to record moving objects.	ICT PoS 5b
Physical Processes (QCA Science Unit 2E)	Find out about and describe the movement of familiar objects. Study the cause and effect of forces in action.	Sc4/2a-c
	Gather information about movement from a range of sources.	ICT PoS 1a
	Present and share ideas about movement in a variety of forms.	ICT PoS 3a
Literacy (Page 8)		
Listening and Responding	Ask and answer questions about how objects move. Conduct an interview with a lorry driver.	En1/2c-e
Understanding and Interpreting Texts	Read, discuss, list and display key topic words. Read information texts and fiction texts about force and movement. Re-tell stories.	En2/1g;2a,c;3b;6a,b
Creating and Shaping Texts	Write instructions, labels and captions related to force and movement. Write information texts about movement including a contents page and glossary. Write persuasive text and imaginative stories after reading stories featuring moving objects.	En3/1d-f
Mathematics (Page 10)		
Using and Applying Mathematics	Explore and record number patterns.	Ma2/2b
	Choose and use appropriate operations and strategies to solve problems about two- and three-wheeled transport.	Ma2/1a-c
Understanding Shape	Observe and describe the position, direction and movement of objects.	Ma3/3a
Measuring	Choose and use appropriate equipment when measuring distances and parts of a bicycles.	Ma3/1b;4a,c
Handling Data	Use tables and charts to sort and organise information.	Ma2/5a

Learning Objectives	Curriculum References
Geography (Page 12)	
Develop geographical skills using globes, maps and plans.	PoS 2c
Identify where places are in the world and movements of imported/exported goods.	PoS 3b
Recognise how places are linked to other parts of the world.	PoS 3e
Plan and use instructions for a programmable toy.	ICT PoS 2c

Learning Objectives	Curriculum References
PSHCE (Page 12)	
Ask and answer questions, interview a guest.	PoS 2a
Explore ideas about personal safety related to road safety and transport.	PoS 3g
Design & Technology (Page 14)	
Generate and develop ideas about moving vehicles and objects, discuss and draw ideas.	PoS 1a–e
Assemble and construct wheeled models using a range of tools, techniques and materials. Use decorative finishing techniques.	QCA D&T Unit 2A PoS 2a,c,d,e
Evaluate the finished product according to original design intention; suggest improvements that could be made.	PoS 3a,b
PE (Page 14)	
Recognise, describe and demonstrate how parts of the body move.	PoS 4b
Create and perform dance sequences.	PoS 6c
Plan and perform basic movements on the floor.	PoS 8a,c,d
Music (Page 14)	
Listen and respond to music that explores movement.	PoS 4b/c/d
Explore and create sounds to show movement.	PoS 1b/c/2a/b
Art (Page 15)	
Design and make images and artefacts connected to wheels.	PoS 2a–c
Record images from first-hand observation of a bicycle.	PoS 1a
Investigate visual and tactile patterns through bicycle tyre rubbings.	PoS 4a
History (Page 15)	
Examine differences between transport now and in the past.	PoS 2b
Use a range of sources to find information on bicycles.	PoS 4a/ICT QCA History Unit 4 PoS 1a
Investigate engineers and their inventions.	PoS 6c
RE (Page 15)	
Discuss the role of Moses in the movement of people from oppression and slavery to freedom in the Promised Land.	PoS 1a;3a,f

Forces and Movement

Science

Starting Points

● Discuss and list wheeled vehicles, objects and toys. What concepts do the children have about how these things move?

● Using digital photographs or images sourced from the Internet, produce a PowerPoint® presentation of a variety of wheeled, moving objects, to be shown on an interactive whiteboard. Children may use an interactive pen to add captions or labels to the slides.

● Read *Duck in the truck* by Jez Alborough (HarperCollins) and identify which forces are being used to move the truck out of the muck. Create a display to show the forces found in the story.

● Ask selected children to bring in a bike, scooter or skateboard from home. Name and discuss the moving parts.

Enquiry

● On the playground, use a wheeled object, such as a bike, to explore the forces involved in movement. Ask, *How do you start a bike moving? How do you speed up, change direction, slow down and stop?* Use a digital camera to record events as they happen and encourage the children to talk about what is happening as they move. Ask the children to present their findings to the class. Use the activity sheet on page 7 to help focus their enquiry.

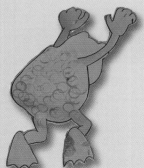

Extension Activities

● Investigate the movement of toy cars down a ramp, changing only one variable such as the height or surface of the ramp. Ask, *What effect does this have on how far the car travels?* Challenge the children to think of and talk about explanations for differences.

● Ask the children to look at the tread on bike or car tyres. *Why do we need a textured surface here?* Introduce the idea of friction and grip. Compare the soles on a range of footwear such as plimsolls, trainers, wellingtons, walking boots and high heels.

On the move!

Pushes and pulls can move things along.

 **time to talk…** Talk about things that move on wheels. How many can you name?

Try it out!

Which one of these will you try out on the playground?

 **think…** How did you start moving? Speed up?
How did you slow down? Stop?
Talk about it and record your ideas here.

 **NOW!** What have you found out about the ways pushes and pulls can move things along?

Literacy

Speaking and Listening

- Interview a long-distance lorry driver or car mechanic about their job. Use a toy microphone and ask the children to generate and write their questions beforehand. Ask the driver to explain how their lorry moves along.

- Play a 'Mastermind' or 'Ask the Expert' game. Take turns to sit in the 'hot seat' and answer questions about how objects, such as a bike, move along.

Reading and Writing

- Ask the children to produce a large, illustrated information poster, including labels and captions about the different parts of their bike and how it moves. Use the activity sheet on page 9 to collect relevant vocabulary.

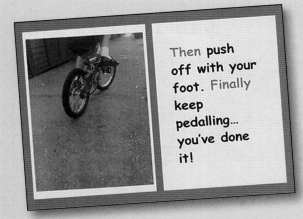

- Write instructions for how to ride a bike. Begin sentences with sequential terms, such as 'First', 'Then', 'Now', 'After that', 'Next' and 'Finally'.

- Make a whole-class big book about movement, including a contents page and a glossary. Small groups of children could be responsible for planning and creating different sections of the book.

- Design a persuasive advert or write a catchy jingle about a new skateboard park that is about to open in your area. The children should include vocabulary related to movement.

- Read and re-tell *Duck in the truck* by Jez Alborough (HarperCollins). Act out the story and use a 'freeze frame' technique to stop and discuss the action at significant moments in the story.

- Read and discuss the sequence of events in *Mrs Armitage on wheels* by Quentin Blake (Picture Lions). Can the children spot the different movement and forces in the story?

- Read non-fiction texts such as *Wheels, wings and other things* by Monica Hughes and Barbara Hunter (Rigby) to identify different types of movement and force.

- Plan and write an imaginative story about a wayward supermarket shopping trolley! The children should use the vocabulary collected about forces and movement.

- Ask the children to use a word processor to write a factual account about moving toys, inserting relevant clip art images into the text.

Label the parts of this bike.

NOW!

Write instructions for how to ride a bike. Start your sentences with the words: First, Next, Then, After that and Finally.

Maths

Using and Applying

● Explore the patterns created when counting on in fours. Start by making a visit to the staff car park and counting the number of car wheels in fours. Record by drawing wheels in groups of four. Look at the number pattern created when counting on in groups of four on a large 100 square.

● Try the bike and trike challenge! Ask, *Is it possible to get a total of nine wheels using just bikes? How about just trikes? What about if a mixture of bikes and trikes were allowed?* Illustrate this example on an interactive whiteboard, using images of bikes and trikes sourced from the Internet. Encourage a logical and systematic procedure to solving the problem. The children could record their working out using drawing, repeated addition number sentences or by using multiplication. You could use real bikes and trikes or use small-scale toy bikes and trikes, such as those in a Playmobil set, for children who need to handle equipment in order to make the calculations. Display your 'problem' questions on the wall with the children's solutions. The activity sheet on page 11 supports this work.

Measuring

● Use metre sticks to measure the distance of toy cars travelling down a ramp (see page 6).

● Use a tape measure to measure the component parts of a bike.

Handling Data

● The children could be asked to spot patterns when counting in twos, for example, two wheels on a bike – all multiples of two are even numbers. Playmobil bikes could be used or children could bring in their own bikes. They could then move on to spot patterns when counting in fours, for example counting car wheels. The numbers should be coloured in on a 100 square and the visual pattern made should be discussed.

● Record data from investigations (such as those above) and use to produce a tally chart. Ask the children to use a graph package, such as *RM Starting First Graph*, to produce and print a graph of results from the investigation.

● Use large PE hoops to sort moving objects into groups, using a range of criteria such as number of wheels.

Forces and Movement

The bike and trike challenge

Can you make a total of nine wheels using:

only bikes?

only trikes?

a mixture of bikes and trikes?

Record your answers by drawing the wheels using a repeated addition number sentence or using multiplication.

NOW! **What if the total was changed to 10? Or 11? Or 12? Show how you worked out your answer.**

Geography

- Discuss the movement of goods imported to our country from all over the world. Ask the children to collect packaging from fruit and vegetables (both tinned and fresh) and begin an investigation about where in the world our food comes from, how many miles it has travelled and how it got here. Find the country of origin on a globe or in an atlas. Use the information collected to create a display with pictures of fruit and the country of origin.

- Look out for country identification letters on cars and lorries, such as 'D' and 'F' and find out which country the letter represents. Carry out a survey in your local area to discover how much traffic has come from different countries. The children could complete the activity sheet on page 13.

- Ask the children to read the label inside their clothing to find out where their clothes were made. Find the country of manufacture in an atlas. Find out whose clothing has travelled the furthest!

- Using a programmable toy, plan and carry out instructions to make the toy move. Decorate the toy as a truck moving around a map or plan of a builder's yard, or as a shopping trolley moving around the mapped aisles of a store.

PSHCE

- Invite a road safety officer or community warden into the class to talk to the children about traffic, road safety and safe places to play.

- Look at protective clothing such as cycle helmets, knee and elbow pads and reflective strips. Talk about why these are important when using bikes, roller skates and skateboards.

Forces and Movement

Have you seen these letter badges on the back of lorries? What do they mean?
Write the names of the countries they represent.

B

P

CH

A

GR

F

D

CZ

E

I

RO

NL

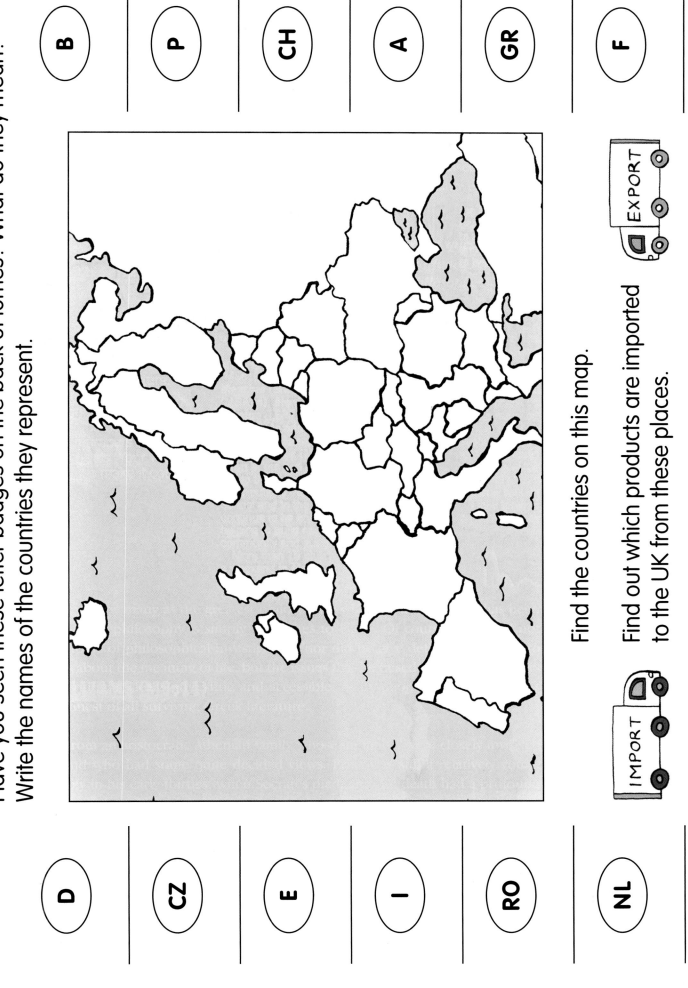

Find the countries on this map.

Find out which products are imported to the UK from these places.

IMPORT

EXPORT

Design & Technology

- Ask the children to generate ideas about moving objects and vehicles by looking at, discussing and drawing them first-hand. You could start by looking at cars parked in the staff car park or ask a recovery vehicle or HGV to park on the playground and use a digital camera to take images of the vehicle. Ask parents to bring in prams and buggies and ask the children to look at how they are constructed.

- Discuss and draw design ideas for a moving model, such as a pick up truck for a favourite character like Bob the Builder, a pram for a doll or teddy, or a shopping trolley for a supermarket. Assemble component parts such as junk boxes, dowels and wooden wheels to construct the model. Paint and decorate the model, referring to the original design sketches. Evaluate the finished product and ask the children to identify successes and suggest one improvement that could be made.

PE

- Ask the children to investigate how our bodies move. Focus their attention on joints such as knees, hips, elbows and shoulders.

- Can the children move in different ways, such as stiffly like a robot or in a fluid, floppy way like a jellyfish? Develop a sequence of movements to music to represent a type of movement.

- Ask the children to suggest different ways to move over, under, around and through a static shape made by a partner.

- Working with a partner, ask the children to make a static shape to illustrate 'push' then 'pull'.

- Have a tug of war contest!

Music

- Listen to 'The little train of Caipira' by Heitor Villa-Lobos (in *Listening to music elements* by Helen MacGregor [A&C Black]) and ask the children to talk about how music has been used to create the effect of movement.

- Use percussion instruments to create a piece of music that represents the movement of a lorry travelling on a bumpy road or a squeaky, troublesome shopping trolley travelling around a supermarket.

- Listen to music featuring a range of tempo, from fast to slow, and discuss the effects used.

Art

- Ask at a cycle shop for old, unwanted wheels and use these as a loom for weaving. Ask the children to weave lengths of wool, ribbon or fabric through the spokes until the wheel has been 'filled' with the woven threads.

- Use modelling materials, such as Plasticine or clay, to create models using pushing, pulling, stretching, twisting, bending and pinching techniques with fingers or modelling tools.

- Make a rubbing from a bicycle or car tyre. Draw the pattern from observation and continue the pattern on a strip of paper.

- Ask the children to make detailed observational drawings of a bicycle.

- Use a story stimulus, such as *Mrs Armitage on wheels* by Quentin Blake (Picture Lions) to generate ideas for 3-D model making.

History

- Ask at your local town library or museum to see and copy images of transportation from the past. Display a collection of images in the classroom. Include images of trams, early buses, steam trains, horse-drawn vehicles and old-fashioned bicycles. Discuss with the children how travel and transport in the past differ from today.

- Create a timeline illustrating the history of the bicycle. What can the children discover about the first bicycles; when were they invented and who invented them?

- Find out about the lives of famous inventors or engineers such as Isambard Kingdom Brunel (1806–1859) or George Stephenson (1781–1848).

RE

- Watch the animated film *The Prince of Egypt* (Dreamworks Home Entertainment). Discuss Moses and the movement of people from slavery in Egypt to the Promised Land.

Electricity

These grids demonstrate the learning objectives covered in the activities within the theme. The curriculum references indicate the relevant programme of study (PoS) for a subject area unless otherwise stated.

	Learning Objectives	Curriculum References
Science (Page 18)		
Scientific Enquiry	Identify areas for investigation relating to circuits.	Sc1/2a
	Plan and conduct experiments about how a circuit works.	Sc1/2b,c,i
	Record findings about circuits in a variety of ways.	Sc1/2g
Physical Processes (QCA Science Unit 2F)	Identify and sort items that use battery power or mains electricity.	Sc4/1a
	Collect and assemble information about electricity.	ICT PoS 1a
	Build and test circuits, explore the use of different components.	Sc4/1b
	Test materials for conductivity in a circuit.	Sc4/1b
	Use a switch to control the flow of electricity.	Sc4/1c
Literacy (Page 20)		
Listening and Responding	Conduct an interview with an electrician.	En1/1c,d;2e
	Ask and answer questions.	En1/2e;3e
Group Discussion and Interaction	Debate the pros and cons of using electricity.	En1/1a-f
Understanding and Interpreting Texts	Read non-fiction texts about electricity.	En2/2a,b
Creating and Shaping Texts	Make a collection of electricity-related words.	En3/2b
	Identify and use rhyming words to create a poem about electricity.	En3/2b
	Write about electricity using organisational features found in published information texts.	En3/1f;2d;9d
	Write text, select and insert images.	ICT PoS 2a;3a
Text Structure and Organisation	Use a planning framework to write an imaginative story about a power cut.	En3/2b-d
Mathematics (Page 22)		
Using and Applying Mathematics	Choose and use the appropriate operation or strategy to solve a problem in an electrical supplies shop.	Ma2/4a
	Solve problems involving money.	Ma2/1a-d;4a
Understanding Shape	Handle a collection of batteries, identify and name their shape.	Ma3/2b
Handling Data	Sort electrical appliances.	Ma2/5a
	Present information in a chart.	Ma2/5a

Electricity

Learning Objectives	Curriculum References
History (Page 24)	
Make a study of the way of life prior to the advent of electricity.	PoS 2b/6b
Learn about the life of a famous British engineer.	QCA History Unit 4 PoS 6c
Gather information about the past from a variety of source material.	PoS 4a/ICT PoS 1a
Geography (Page 24)	
Identify power stations and other places on a map.	PoS 2c
Describe the location and impact of power stations.	PoS 3a;4a
Consider the environmental effects of electricity production.	PoS 4b;5a,b
Gather information from first hand and secondary sources.	PoS 1b;2d/ICT PoS 1a
Design & Technology (Page 26)	
Disassemble electrical games to ascertain how they work.	PoS 5a
Generate design ideas to create a buzzer game.	PoS 1e
Art (Page 26)	
Choose images associated with electricity and develop initial ideas.	PoS 1b
Use own designs to create a product.	PoS 2c
Music (Page 26)	
Listen to and appraise music suggestive of lightning storms.	PoS 4a;5d
Pinpoint how musical elements have been used to create effects.	PoS 4b
Compose, rehearse and perform 'electrical storm' music.	PoS 2a,b
PSHCE (Page 27)	
Identify and discuss hazards associated with electricity.	PoS 3g
Establish a set of safety rules.	PoS 3g
Encourage others to make safe choices.	PoS 3g
PE (Page 27)	
Respond to electrical storm sound effects and music stimuli in dance.	PoS 6a
Explore and perform movements, combine to form a 'storm' dance sequence.	PoS 6a-d

Electricity

Science

Starting Points

● Find out what the children already know about electricity and establish possible lines of enquiry.

● Present the children with a large collection of batteries, wires, crocodile clips, bulbs and bulb holders and allow a child-led exploration session. Can anyone discover how to make the bulb light? Share findings in a whole class feedback discussion. The children could complete the activity sheet on page 19.

● Ask the children to sit in a circle, holding hands. Pass a hand squeeze from child to child around the circle, likening this to the way a circuit works. Ask one child to break the 'circuit' by not holding hands and talk about what happens as a result. Explain how a switch works by breaking and completing a circuit.

● Make and display a class collection of electricity words.

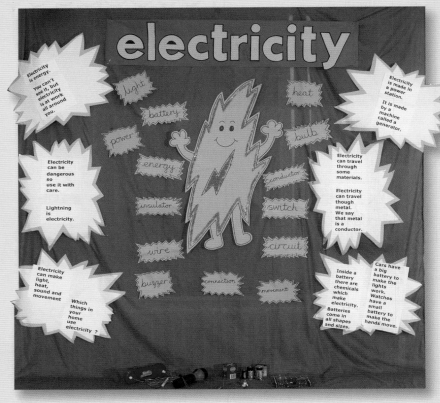

Enquiry

● Pose the question, *Can electricity travel through all materials?* Show the children a selection of everyday items (plastic bottle top, cork, teaspoon, glove, cup, coin). Establish the materials that the items are made from. Ask the children to predict whether or not electricity will be able to pass through them. *How could we find out?* Lead the thinking towards including one item at a time into a working circuit.

● Make a circuit and show that the bulb is lit. Ask the children to test the items one by one by attaching the items into the circuit and seeing whether or not the bulb will light. Discuss the results and introduce the term 'conductor'. What can be concluded about the conductivity of materials?

Extension Activities

● Having established that metal will allow electricity to flow through it, refine the experiment by testing different samples of metal such as copper, zinc, steel, aluminium and silver to discover if these metals are conductors.

● Ask the children to find the point in their house where electricity enters. Ask, *How does electricity get from the power station to our homes?*

● Sort electrical items into those that use batteries and those that use mains electricity. Sort electrical items into those that use electricity to make heat, light, movement or sound.

Circuit Circus

Make a circuit for each of the circus performers using only the equipment shown.

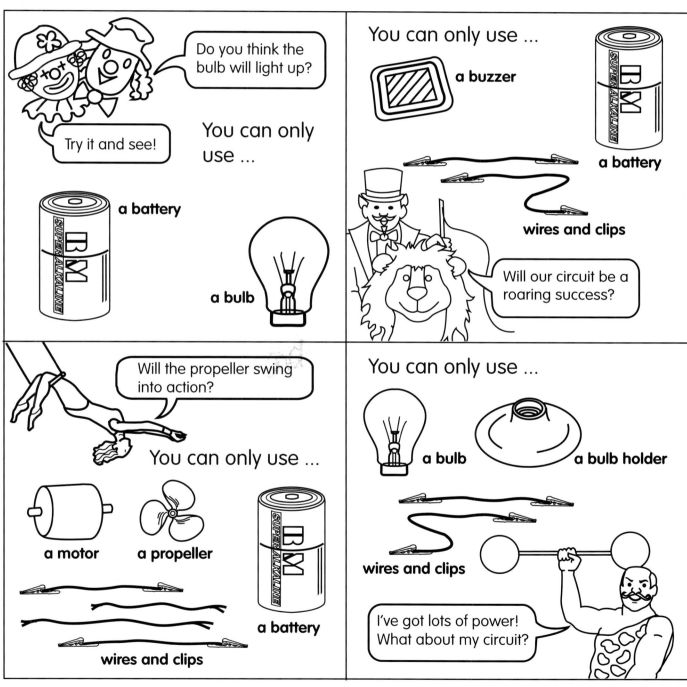

Do you think the bulb will light up?

Try it and see!

You can only use ...

a battery

a bulb

You can only use ...

a buzzer

a battery

wires and clips

Will our circuit be a roaring success?

Will the propeller swing into action?

You can only use ...

a motor

a propeller

a battery

wires and clips

You can only use ...

a bulb

a bulb holder

wires and clips

I've got lots of power! What about my circuit?

NOW! Take a photo of the circuits you have made. Write about what happened.

Literacy

Speaking and Listening

- Invite an electrician to come and talk to the class about their job. Have an 'Ask the expert' question and answer session with members of the class.

- Have a class debate about the pros and cons of using electricity. **Pros:** Electricity provides the energy for many household appliances, which means we no longer have to do chores, such as washing clothes, by hand. Electricity enables us to store food safely and conveniently in fridges and freezers. Electricity is used to power our entertainments, such as radios, CD players and televisions. Electric light is much safer than candlelight. The electricity industry provides lots of jobs for people. **Cons:** Power stations and pylons are ugly blots on the landscape. People are overly-reliant on using electrical gadgets for entertainment, children spend too much time looking at the TV and playing computer games. Generating electricity is adding to the problem of global warming. Electricity can be dangerous: people can get electric shocks.

Reading and Writing

- Read non-fiction texts, such as *Find out about: electricity* by Terry Jennings (BBC Books) and *Electricity* by Linda Howe (HarperCollins).

- Write a diary entry about a day in the life of a child in the times before electricity.

- Write a story about a power cut with a dramatic and exciting climax! Provide a planning frame for the children to use as a starting point.

- Write rhyming verse about the uses for electricity. This work can be used to create a class display. Dressing-up clothes and a pair of child's wellington boots can be used to make an electrician figure to go on the display.

- Use a word processor to design, write and print an information leaflet about electricity. The children could insert graphics into the text and experiment with different font sizes and styles.

- The children could complete the word search on the activity sheet on page 21. The children also need to think about rhyming words.

Wordsearch

Can you find these electricity words?

e	a	c	i	r	c	u	i	t	e
o	l	b	u	l	b	d	p	e	l
c	q	e	h	y	b	w	i	r	e
e	a	k	c	l	i	p	t	i	c
n	j	m	i	t	b	h	c	d	t
e	l	e	c	t	r	i	f	d	r
r	s	t	g	c	r	k	r	a	i
g	b	a	t	t	e	r	y	n	c
y	i	l	c	j	e	a	k	g	i
l	p	o	w	e	r	p	m	e	t
x	l	v	f	g	f	s	m	r	y
c	o	n	d	u	c	t	o	r	n

bulb

wire

battery

circuit

spark

clip

energy

conductor

metal

power

danger

Can you find the word (electricity?)

Can you think of rhyming words for these electrical words?

spark	wire	power
_____	_____	_____
_____	_____	_____
_____	_____	_____

NOW! **Use your rhyming words to make a poem.**

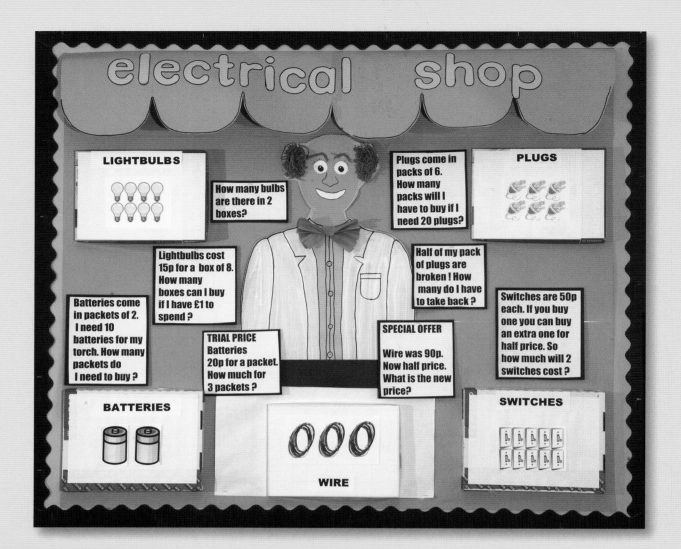

Maths

Using and Applying

● Use the context of an electrical supplies shop to pose two-step problem solving activities involving addition, multiplication and division. This could become the basis of a display as seen above. Use coins to find different ways to make a set amount. Use subtraction to calculate the change needed from £1. Provide the children with the activity sheet on page 23 to complete.

● Ask the children to find out how many units of electricity their household uses in a 24-hour period.

Understanding Shape

● Look at and handle a collection of batteries and sort them according to their shape, for example cuboid and cylinder. Encourage the children to describe the properties of the shapes as they handle the items.

Handling Data

● Use sorting hoops to arrange electrical items into two sets according to whether they use mains electricity or battery power. Overlap the hoops to create a large Venn diagram. Place items which can use both mains and battery in the central overlapping section.

● Compare data on units of electricity that the children's households use. Compile a whole-class block graph illustrating units of electricity used.

Switches are 50p each. If you buy one you can buy an extra one for half price. So how much will 2 switches cost ?

THE ELECTRICAL SUPPLIES SHOP

OPEN

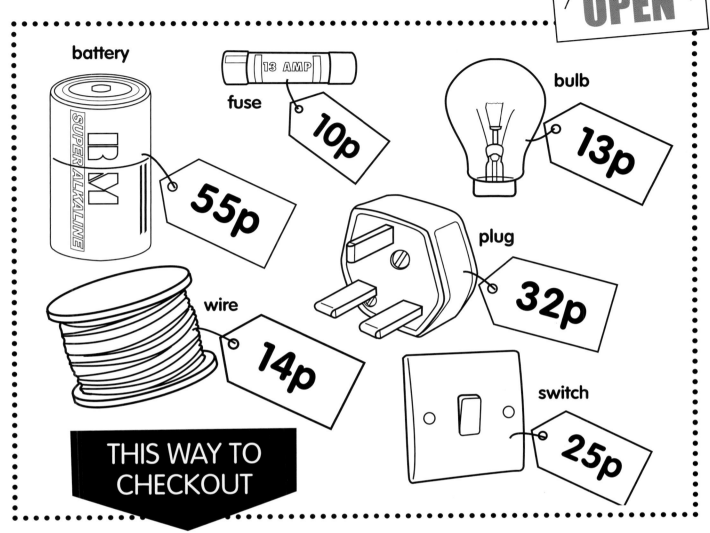

battery

fuse

bulb

55p

10p

13p

plug

32p

wire

14p

switch

25p

THIS WAY TO CHECKOUT

Choose three items. Add the amounts together to find the total cost. Show your working on a separate sheet of paper.

You have £1 to spend in the shop. Buy as many different items as you can. Show how you worked out your answer.

Calculate the difference between the most expensive and the least expensive item.

How many bulbs can you buy for £1? How much change would you have? What if you had £2 to spend?

If you buy one plug you can get another one for half price. Find out how much two plugs would cost.

SALE!
Everything in the shop has been reduced by 5p. What is the new price of each item?

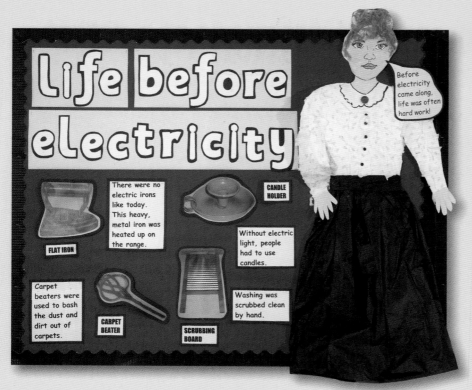

- Investigate how people generated power and made machines operate before the advent of electricity. Talk about the use of steam-powered trains, windmills and watermills, and the use of animals.

- Find out what life was like in the average household before electricity. Collect artefacts such as a flat iron, a copper kettle, an enamelled candle holder, an oil lamp and a carpet beater. Use pictures and facts to create a display based on life before electricity.

- Ask the children to think about how different their day would be if they couldn't use electricity. Discuss which electrical items they would miss the most. Why not try it out for a day!

- Compare artefacts from the past to their modern day equivalent, for example comparing a flat iron to an electric steam iron.

- Watch a DVD (such as BBC *Magical Grandad: famous people 2*) about domestic life before electricity, or about the life and times of an engineer, such as Isambard Kingdom Brunel (1806–1859) working in the age of steam.

Geography

- Talk about how electricity is produced. Ask the children to locate the nearest power station to their home on a map of the local area. How is the power station fuelled?

- Discuss the impact that the power station has in its locality, in terms of, for example, employment, pollution and traffic.

- Encourage the children to talk about how they think electricity travels from the power station to our homes. Use drawings or photos (which could be sourced from the Internet) to illustrate the steps in the journey of electricity. Children could also complete the activity sheet on page 25.

- Ask the children to identify other sources of generating electricity, such as through the use of tidal power, solar panels on a roof or an offshore wind farm. Discuss and identify some advantages and disadvantages of these systems.

THE JOURNEY OF ELECTRICITY

Where does electricity come from? How does it get to your house?

Put these pictures in the correct order. You will need scissors, glue and a strip of paper. When you have stuck the pictures write a caption beneath each one, to explain each stage of the journey.

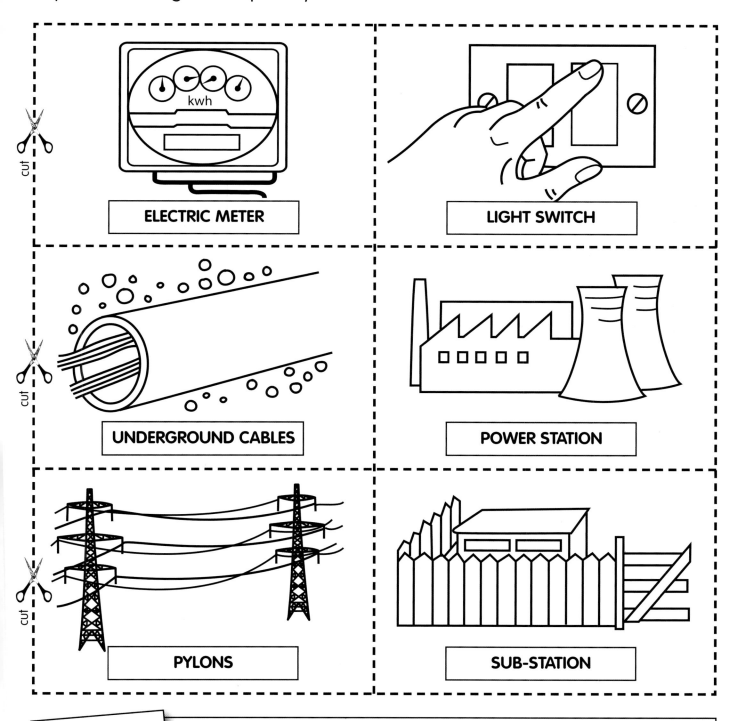

ELECTRIC METER

LIGHT SWITCH

UNDERGROUND CABLES

POWER STATION

PYLONS

SUB-STATION

cut

NOW! Can you locate the power station which is nearest to your home?

Design & Technology

- Look at and play with an electric buzzer game from a toy shop. If possible, disassemble the toy to see how it has been made. Discuss how the toy works and identify that the electrical circuit is made whole when the wire 'wand' touches the shaped wire.

- Design and make a similar buzzer game, using wire, a battery and a buzzer, as shown to the right.

Art

- Choose one image associated with electricity, such as a light bulb. Use a photocopier to reproduce the image, exploring changing the size of the image or using different coloured paper. Explore different ways in which the images of the light bulb could be assembled, in terms of orientation, colour and pattern, and design. Select and create an artwork made from the images, as shown below.

- Using music or sound effects as a stimulus, create an image that is evocative of an electric storm. Work on a large scale and use highly-contrasting colours to create the feeling of power and energy.

Music

- Listen to and discuss pieces of music in which the composer has used musical effects to suggest an electrical lightning storm, such as *Thunder and lightning polka* by Johann Strauss II or *The rite of spring* by Igor Stravinsky.

- Ask the children to create their own music using percussion instruments that represent a lightning storm.

Electricity

PSHCE

- Watch and discuss a DVD about electricity and electrical safety, such as *Cats eyes: electricity, light and sound* (BBC Primary Science Plus video pack). Free resources can be obtained from the Electrical Safety Council, via their website www.switchedonkids.org.uk

- Ask adults to pose in photographs, making 'safety mistakes' with electrical items. Show the photographs to children and ask them to identify what the adults are doing wrong. Create a display with the photos and children's comments.

- Ask the children to present some informative safety guidelines for another class in the school.

PE

- Listen to a sound-effects CD featuring an electric storm, such as *Sound Effects Volume 2–Nature and Animals*, focus listening on the explosive bangs and cracks made by lightning. Working in pairs, children could explore movements and shapes that interpret the sound of lightning. Develop ideas into a dance sequence, performed to appropriate sound effects or music.

Health and Growth

These grids demonstrate the learning objectives covered in the activities within the theme. The curriculum references indicate the relevant programme of study (PoS) for a subject area unless otherwise stated.

	Learning Objectives	Curriculum References
Science (Page 30)		
Scientific Enquiry	Pose and discuss questions about health and decide how to answer them.	Sc1/2a
	Make observations about pulse rate and record results.	Sc1/2f/ICT PoS 1b
Life Processes and Living Things (QCA Science Unit 2A)	Confirm that eating food and drinking water are essential for human life.	Sc2/2b
	Sort foods into groups according to given criteria.	Sc2/2c
	Identify foods which are important for growth in childhood.	Sc2/2c
	Explain how exercise keeps humans healthy.	Sc2/2c
Literacy (Page 32)		
Speaking	Discuss key points in a story about growing.	En1/1d
	Recite a poem about growth.	En1/1a;8b
Listening and Responding	Organise and ask questions in an interview with a mother and child.	En1/2d,e
Understanding and Interpreting Texts	Read poems and use as a model for own poem about growing up.	En3/1f
Engaging With and Responding to Texts	Identify and comment on key points in a story about growing.	En2/1lm
Creating and Shaping Texts	Write an advertisement for a keep fit club using descriptive and persuasive language.	En3/1a
	Write captions for a 'map' of a well known story.	En3/1b
	Write notes describing a story character.	En3/2b
Mathematics (Page 34)		
Using and Applying Mathematics	Choose an appropriate operation to calculate the difference between two numbers.	Ma2/1c;4a
Knowing and Using Number Facts	Use doubling to create a growing number sequence.	Ma2/2b
Measuring	Correctly use the words centimetre, metre, grams and kilograms when measuring.	Ma3/1d
	Use equipment such as tape measures, metre sticks and weighing scales.	Ma3/4a,c
Handling Data	Collect data about height and weight. Create a database.	Ma2/5a/ICT PoS 1b
	Use information to answer problems about changes in growth.	Ma2/4a

Health and Growth

Learning Objectives	Curriculum References
PSHCE (Page 36)	
Discuss health and food options and make positive choices.	PoS 2c
Highlight the benefits of exercise and healthy eating.	PoS 3a
Follow basic hygiene procedures.	PoS 3b
Art (Page 38)	
Use printing techniques to produce a large image representing growth.	PoS 2a-c
Create work in 3-D using mouldable materials.	PoS 5b
Geography (Page 38)	
Identify foods grown in the Mediterranean region including those exported to our country.	PoS 3e
Use a globe or map to locate Mediterranean countries.	PoS 2c;3b
Make comparisons between our own and a Mediterranean climate.	PoS 3d
History (Page 38)	
Ask and answer questions about food preferences in the past.	PoS 4b
Explain why certain foods were not available at different times.	PoS 2b
Investigate attitudes towards food and health in the past and compare to modern day convictions.	PoS 2a, b
Find out about a famous person from the past such as Edward Jenner.	QCA History Unit 4 PoS 6c
PE (Page 39)	
Identify how exercise plays an important role in overall fitness and health.	PoS 4a
Recognise the changes that occur in one's body during and after exercise.	PoS 4b
Describe to others the changes that take place.	PoS 4b
Music (Page 39)	
Use a known melody as a template for creating and composing a song about growth.	PoS 2a,b;5b
Rehearse and perform a composition.	PoS 5a,c
Design & Technology (Page 39)	
Generate ideas about fruit drinks, evaluate commercial products.	PoS 1a,c;5a
Design and make food products such as smoothies.	PoS 5c
Keep hands and equipment clean and safe to use.	PoS 2f

Science

Starting Points

- Discuss what would happen if we didn't eat or drink. Ask, *How long can a human survive without water or food? What would happen to our bodies if we never took any exercise?* Use a variety of information sources, including books, video, CD-ROMs and the Internet.

- Discuss why we need to eat a varied diet to stay healthy. Sort a selection of food items or images into a pyramid, with 'treat' foods that we can eat a little of at the top of the pyramid and essential foods that we can eat a lot of at the bottom.

- Ask the children to consider why milk and dairy products are important for children. Use skeleton pictures and information about dairy products to create a class display.

Enquiry

- Investigate the effect of exercise on our bodies, focusing primarily on heart rate. Explain that the heart is a muscle and talk about its function as a pump. Explain that as we exercise, our hearts need to work harder and faster to pump blood around our bodies to provide oxygen and 'fuel' for the muscles, which are moving.

- Using a pulse meter, ask the children to record their pulse after being engaged in different activities. Start with resting, then gentle exercise such as walking, and then more vigorous exercise such as skipping or running. Ask the children to compare their pulse rate after the different activities and explain in their own words why these differences occur.

- Ask the children to make written notes about any changes in their bodies that they notice during or after exercise. This might include changes in their breathing, the colour of their face, sweating, or an aching sensation in their muscles. Encourage the children to think about why these changes happen; *Why do we breathe faster? Why do we sweat? Why might our faces appear flushed?* The activity sheet on page 31 supports this work.

Extension Activities

- Ask the children to consider why it is important to carry out warm-up activities before doing physical exercise.

- Discuss why it is important to wash our bodies after sustained exercise.

MIGHTY  MUSCLE!

Did you know that your heart is a muscle? It needs a good work out, just like the other muscles in your body. Find out what happens to your heart rate when you exercise.

Use a pulse meter to find out how hard your heart is working when you are doing the following:

RESTING

Sit and look at a book for two minutes.

My pulse rate is [heart] beats per minute

WALKING

Walk around for two minutes at a normal pace.

My pulse rate is [heart] beats per minute

SKIPPING

Skip with a rope for two minutes.

My pulse rate is [heart] beats per minute

RUNNING

Run as fast as you can for two minutes.

My pulse rate is [heart] beats per minute

NOW!

Did you notice any other changes in your body after exercising? What did your face look like? How did your skin feel? How about your breathing? How did your legs feel?

Literacy

Speaking and Listening

● Read *You'll soon grow into them, Titch* by Pat Hutchins (HarperTrophy). Discuss the key points in the story. Use a 'hot seating' technique to explore ideas about how Titch might be feeling during the story (refer to the activity sheet on page 33).

● Ask the children to act out the story, stopping the action at certain points to talk about what has just happened and what will happen next.

● Ask the children to talk about their own experiences of growing up. Ask, *What are you looking forward to doing when you are older?*

● Interview a mum with a baby. Write out questions in advance, using 'Who', 'When', 'What', 'Why' and 'How' questions.

Reading and Writing

● Write notes describing Titch on stick-it notes and attach around an enlarged picture of him.

● Read the poem 'The end' in *Now we are six* by AA Milne (Methuen). Ask the children to learn to recite the poem by heart. Highlight the rhyming words in the poem. Ask the children to plan and write their own poem about growing up, using a similar rhyming couplet style.

● Ask the children to write an advert for a new 'Kids' Keep Fit Club', opening in the local area.

● Make a story map, using sequential words, to illustrate the key points in the Titch story (the activity sheet on page 33 should be provided). Using a word-processing package, ask the children to type and print labels describing the different parts of the story for a classroom display about Titch.

About Titch

Read the story *You'll soon grow into them, Titch* by Pat Hutchins. Write the key points in this story map.

1. At first …	2. After that …	3. Next …
4. In a while …	5. Then …	6. Finally …

NOW!

**Choose someone in your class to pretend they are Titch.
Sit them in the 'hot seat' and ask them how it feels to be Titch.**

Maths

Using and Applying

● Provide the activity sheet on page 35 and ask the children to find out who is the shortest and the tallest person in the school. They will need to find the difference between the two figures, using either subtraction or counting on from the smaller number. A display can then be created to show their findings.

Using Number Facts

● Investigate how quickly a number can 'grow' through the process of doubling. Demonstrate by starting with 1, 2, 4, 8, 16 and 32. Ask, *How far can you continue to double? How many steps would it take to reach a three-digit number?* Ask the children to predict, then try it out. What do they notice about the numbers generated?

Measuring

● Working in pairs, ask the children to measure the height and weight of everyone in the class. Record the data and return to the figures at the end of the academic year. Has anyone grown in height or weight? Note the changes that have taken place. It will be necessary here to be sensitive when discussing and comparing children's weights.

● Encourage the children to start recording their height on each successive birthday.

● Ask the children to find out how much they weighed at birth. Compare this to their current weight.

Handling Data

● Ask the children to find out the weight, height and ages of people in their family. They should list the figures in ascending order. Encourage the children to ask and answer questions about their data: *Is the oldest person also the tallest? Does the tallest person weigh the most?*

● Ask the children to carry out a survey of favourite PE activities recording responses on a tally chart. Demonstrate, using a graph package, how to produce a graph of results. Discuss the advantages and the limitations of such a graph.

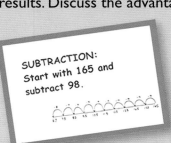

FIND THE DIFFERENCE

Find the shortest and the tallest person in your school. Measure their height with a tape measure or metre stick.

I'm shortest!

The shortest person is

They are _____ cm tall.

The tallest person is

They are _____ cm tall.

I'm tallest!

SHORTEST

TALLEST

Calculate the difference in their heights using subtraction. Start with the biggest number and take away the smallest number. Write your number sentence here:

☐ cm − ☐ cm = ☐ cm

Show how you worked out your answer here:

NOW! Can you use a counting-on method to find the difference? Which method do you prefer?

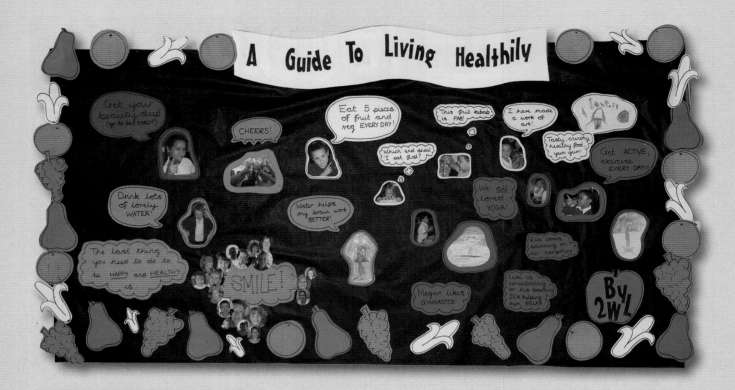

PSHCE

- Present the children with packaging from an assortment of snacks. Using large sorting hoops, ask the children to sort the products according to whether they are 'healthy' or 'unhealthy'. Encourage children to give reasons for their choices. Promote the healthier options, explaining why they are better for us.

- Debate with the children the role and effect of 'junk food' advertising aimed at children. Ask, *Should such adverts be banned? Why do fast food restaurants give away free toys and games with their food?*

- Through role play, model a good, effective hand washing routine. Repeat and ask the children to join in. Talk about the importance of washing hands after going to the toilet and before eating.

- Ask the children to complete the activity sheet on page 37. Then, create a class display that mirrors the activity sheet. Divide a large circle into five sections, then paint each section. The children should then collage or draw pictures to go in the relevant section.

- Ask the children to think of what they can do to lead a healthy life. Photograph the children and create a display using their pictures and their ideas.

HAPPY HEALTHY HENRY

If you want to stay healthy, just follow my advice. Make sure that every day you: **wash, eat a balanced diet, drink, exercise and sleep.**

Draw a picture showing yourself doing each of these things.

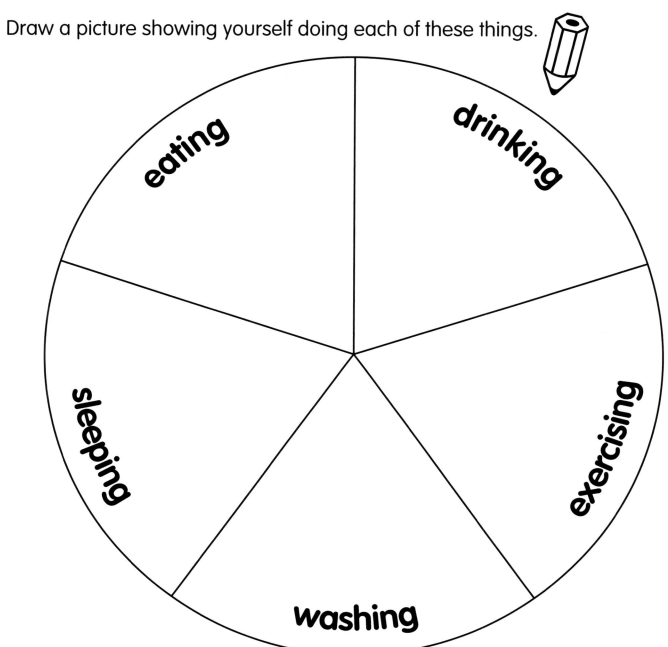

eating

drinking

sleeping

exercising

washing

NOW! Imagine that Happy Healthy Henry is coming to visit you. Write or talk about the healthy things you could do together.

Art

● Make handprint artwork consisting of concentric circles, showing growth in size of hands, from younger children to older children on the outer edge, as shown here in the display.

● Use Modroc to create 3-D sculptures of hands from children in different year groups.

Geography

● The Mediterranean diet has a reputation for being a healthy and nutritious one. Ask the children to identify the Mediterranean Sea on a map. Find out which countries make up 'the Mediterranean'. Discuss the food products that are grown or harvested in this area. Choose some examples, such as olives, oranges and grapes. Ask the children to find out about the Mediterranean climate and the effect it has on the growing season and availability of these foods. Ask, *How is the Mediterranean climate different to our own?*

History

● Find out about attitudes towards healthy foods through the ages. *Why did the Romans think brown bread was inferior to white? What did the Elizabethans do with potatoes before they realised they could be cooked and eaten? What did invalid Victorians drink at the seaside? Why were citrus fruits and bananas considered luxury items in the 1940s?*

● Find out about a famous person from the past who has played a role in developing medicines to keep us healthy. The class could focus on Edward Jenner (1749–1823), who pioneered the use of vaccinations, or Alexander Fleming (1881–1955), who discovered the use of penicillin as an antibiotic.

● Investigate life expectancy through the ages. Consider the reasons for the increase in the human lifespan.

Health and Growth

PE

- With the children working in pairs or small groups, ask them to undertake a range of activities, which could be arranged in 'stations' around a hall or open space. These could include skipping with a rope, jumping in and out of a series of hoops and stepping up and down on a low bench or box. The children should talk about how they feel before and after each activity.

- Discuss with the children the importance of staying fit and healthy and the need for daily physical exercise. Discuss what children could do to become more active in their everyday life, for example walking to school. Create a display to promote their ideas.

Music

- As a class, compose lyrics for a song about healthy living or growing up. You could use the tune of a well known song or nursery rhyme as a starting point or compose an original score for the song. After rehearsing, the song could be performed to another class or during an assembly.

Design & Technology

- Evaluate a selection of fruit smoothies available from a supermarket. Ask the children to decide on the criteria upon which they will be judged or graded. Children could then design and make their own smoothie.

- Design and make a yogurt by adding the children's choice of fresh fruit, dried fruit, nuts and cereals to plain natural yogurt. Organise a 'blind' taste testing session to compare the home made product with a branded commercially available one.

Grouping and Changing Materials

These grids demonstrate the learning objectives covered in the activities within the theme. The curriculum references indicate the relevant programme of study (PoS) for a subject area unless otherwise stated.

	Learning Objectives	Curriculum References
Science (Page 42)		
Scientific Enquiry	Plan and carry out investigations about changing materials, predicting possible outcomes.	Sc1/2a-c
	Make and record observations.	Sc1/2f
	Record and store images using a digital camera.	ICT PoS 1b
	Discuss results and draw conclusions. Evaluate the success of the investigation or enquiry in answering initial questions posed.	Sc1/2h,i,j
Materials and their Properties (QCA Science Unit 2A)	Sort items according to the material from which they have been made.	Sc3/1b
	Identify naturally occurring materials such as those that derive from an animal or a plant.	Sc3/1c
	Investigate how materials can be changed by processes such as heating and cooling.	Sc3/2b
	Explore whether changes can be reversed or if they are permanent.	Sc3/2b
Literacy (Page 44)		
Group Discussion and Interaction	Generate ideas about materials by discussing plans and lines of enquiry with others.	En1/1c;2d
	Take turns in speaking.	En1/3a
Creating and Shaping Texts	Use information texts as a model for own writing about materials.	En3/1f
	Write a class book about materials in collaboration with others.	En3/2d
	Use bullet points or alphabetical order to structure and organise text.	En3/1d
	Write instructions and recipes.	En3/9a,d
	Read non-fiction texts about materials.	En2/2a,b;7b
	Use organisational features when reading for information.	En2/1m;2a
Mathematics (Page 46)		
Counting and Understanding Number	Identify the pattern of calibrated numbers on a thermometer.	Ma2/2b
	Extend the pattern of numbers using the same multiple.	Ma2/2b
	Read numbers from a calibrated scale and place in the correct numerical order to 100.	Ma2/2c
Measuring	Use weighing scales in practical activities to measure weight in grams.	Ma3/4a,c
	Use a thermometer to measure temperature change.	Ma3/4c
	Measure the duration of an activity or experiment using standard units of time.	Ma3/4a

Learning Objectives	Curriculum References
Geography (Page 48)	
Use maps to locate places in the UK and in the wider world connected with raw materials or manufacturing.	PoS 2c;3b
Identify changes to materials in the natural environment and suggest reasons for change.	PoS 4b;5a
Ask questions about everyday items in terms of what materials they have been made from and the processes involved in their manufacture.	PoS 1a
History (Page 48)	
Identify the materials used to make products such as clothes or toys, over time.	PoS 4a,b
Identify differences and similarities in products from the present day and the past.	PoS 2b
Give reasons for the change in usage of certain materials.	PoS 2a
Find out about manufacturing industry in the past and the way of life for the workforce.	PoS 4a,b;6b
Art (Page 50)	
Use a variety of processes to change the state of materials.	PoS 2b
Create 3-D artefacts with materials that change in state.	PoS 5b
Use naturally occurring materials as a starting point for an image.	PoS 5a
Design & Technology (Page 50)	
Generate ideas about changes in food products when raw and cooked.	PoS 1a,c
Design and make food products.	PoS 5c
Follow instructions and recipes to combine ingredients.	PoS 2d
RE (Page 51)	
Read and discuss 'miracle' stories from Christianity and other religions.	PoS 1a;3a,f
PSHCE (Page 51)	
Discuss the responsibilities we all share in caring for our environment, both on a local and a global scale.	PoS 2g
Recognise the impact of the choices we make.	PoS 2c
Music (Page 51)	
Identify how sounds can differ according to the materials used in the making of instruments.	PoS 4c
Ascertain how a particular material has been used to create a particular musical timbre.	PoS 4b

Grouping and Changing Materials

Starting Points

- Discuss the changes that occur to materials when they are heated or cooled, for example in the kitchen. Observe and compare the differences between raw and cooked egg, change a slice of bread into toast, melt solid chunks of chocolate into liquid. Create a display showing the experiments.

Enquiry

- Discuss with the children the effects of freezing water. Ask, *Do you think this change will occur in other liquids too? Can you name some other liquids?* Talk about what might happen to these liquids if they were placed in a freezer and left for a period of time.

- Show the children a collection of liquids, such as vinegar, milk, olive oil, lemonade and fruit juice. Place a small, measured quantity of each liquid in a transparent plastic food bag and secure with a knot. Use a digital camera to take pre-test photos of each bag. Explain that the bags will be placed in a freezer and left overnight. Ask the children to predict what might happen to each of the liquids. Consider the changes that took place when water was frozen into ice. Talk about possible changes to the size, feel, colour or smell of the liquids to be tested. Children should complete the activity sheet on page 43.

- Remove the bags from the freezer the following day and examine what has happened to the contents. Use a digital camera to photograph the results of the freezing. Were any of the predictions correct? Are the changes that have occurred reversible or irreversible? Leave the food bags in a warm place and make a note of any changes that take place over the course of an hour or a morning.

Extension Activities

- Review the 'kitchen science' activities (from Starting Points) and sort the changes into reversible or irreversible. Predict what might happen to other household substances when they are cooled or heated.

- Identify other agents of change, for example what happens to egg white when it is infused with air through whisking? What happens to the exposed flesh of an apple when it is left in the air? What happens to an iron nail when it is left exposed in damp air?

Freezing

Investigate what happens to these liquids when you freeze them:

LIQUID TESTED	PREDICTION What do you think will happen?	RESULT What actually happened?
vinegar		
milk		
orange juice		
olive oil		
lemonade		

 **NOW!** Take a photo of what has happened to these liquids.

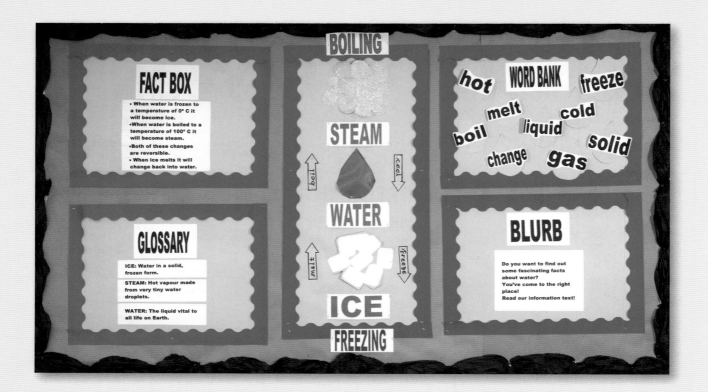

Literacy

Speaking and Listening

- Using a prop, such as a toy microphone or telephone, ask the children to talk to each other about their learning, following a practical investigation, such as the enquiry on page 42.

Reading and Writing

- Look at a selection of non-fiction texts about materials and identify the features of the book, such as a contents page, index and glossary.

- Create a whole-class big book, containing the features of an information text, on the theme of changing materials. Children working collaboratively in small groups could each be responsible for one section of the book.

- Collect and display a word bank of vocabulary related to materials. Challenge the children to compose a definition for each of the words. Children should complete the activity sheet on page 45. The literacy work for this topic could be combined to create a class display, as above.

- Compile a class A to Z list of materials.

- Read recipes and identify the verbs used in the instructions. Highlight the use of temporal sequencing language, such as, 'Then', 'Next', 'After that' and 'Finally'.

- Write out a recipe, highlighting with colour all of the words that describe a change, such as mix, whisk, combine, bake.

- Use bullet points as a device for organising text on a poster outlining the potential hazards in a hot, steamy kitchen.

- Challenge the children to write a story about a new pupil who has the power to change their body into a liquid or an elastic state.

Glossary

Write a sentence to explain each of these words:

boil	
ice	
liquid	
melt	
solid	
steam	

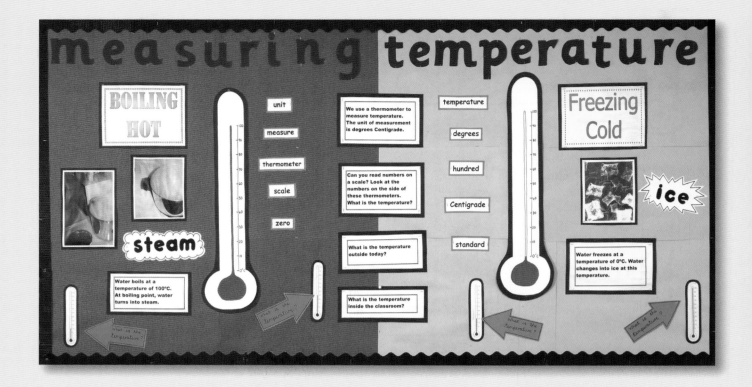

Maths

Using and Applying

● Change numbers using a function machine, for example explore the effects of halving or doubling. Investigate a general statement, such as 'When I halve a multiple of 10, the answer is always an even number'.

Counting and Understanding Numbers

● Rehearse the skill of reading numbers on a scale by reading temperatures shown on a thermometer. Place a series of temperature readings in correct numerical order.

● Look at how thermometers are calibrated, for example in multiples of 5 or 10. Write down a continuation of the number pattern created, extending the sequence by another 5 or 10 numbers. Provide the activity sheet on page 47 for children to complete.

● A display of thermometers could be created with questions relating to temperature. Children could search for photos on the Internet of ice and steam to add to the display.

Measuring

● Use weighing scales to measure ingredients in grams when cooking cakes or bread.

● Record the time taken for an ice cube to melt.

Measuring temperature

Water boils at
100°C

Water freezes at
0°C

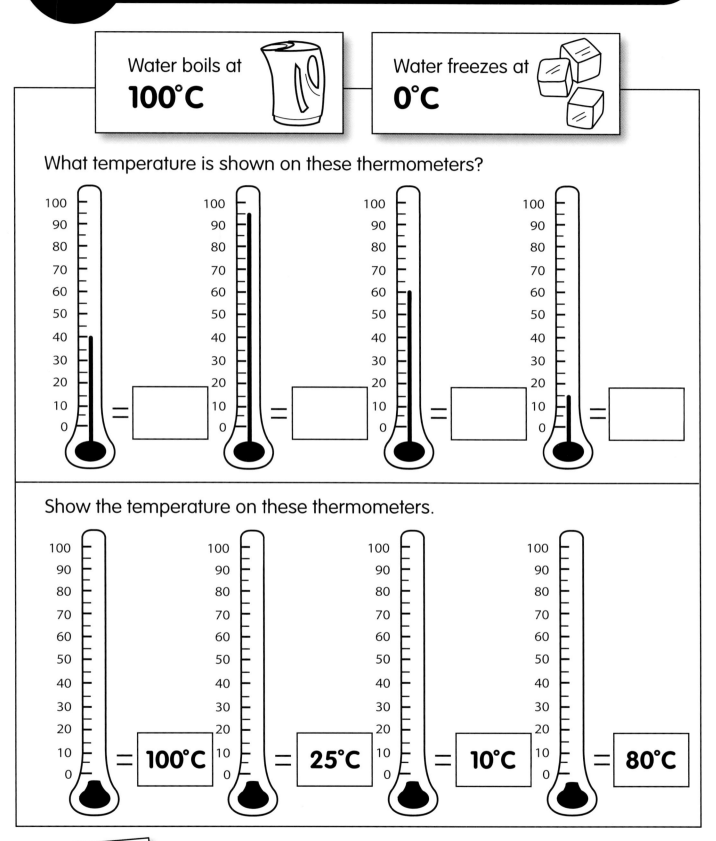

What temperature is shown on these thermometers?

What is the temperature of your classroom?

Geography

- Sort materials, such as paper, wool, feathers, leather, cotton and rubber, into two sets: those which have derived from an animal and those which have been made from a plant.

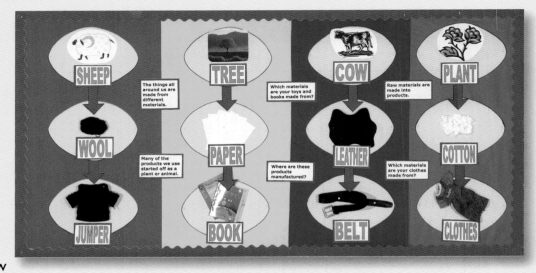

- Focus on one item, such as a leather belt, and document its 'journey' from raw material to finished product. Identify the different stages of its manufacture and the various jobs that people do in the process of making the item. Provide the children with the activity sheet on page 49 to complete. Using photos, drawn pictures or the actual items create a display. The display should show the production of each item.

- Name and locate industrial and manufacturing towns and cities on a map of the United Kingdom. Arrange a visit to a manufacturing site, if one exists in your local area.

- Locate on a globe the country of origin of raw materials imported to our country, such as steel from India, cotton from North America and hardwood from Indonesia.

- Identify naturally occurring raw materials in your locality, such as gravel pits, a clay quarry, a coal mine, slate workings, reed beds and coppiced woodland. Talk about how these materials are developed into products.

- Identify features in the locality where physical changes have occurred to materials in the environment over time, such as the erosion of a chalk cliff, the weathering of an exposed rock, the creation of limestone stalagmites and stalactites in a cavern.

- How does the planet Earth change materials? Investigate the changes caused to materials by volcanic eruption, such as with molten rock becoming solidified.

History

- Investigate how the usage of materials to make everyday items, such as clothes, toys or kitchen utensils, has changed over time.

- Create a photographic or pictorial timeline highlighting the materials used, for example a sequence showing toys from the Roman era being made from bone or horn, toys in the Middle Ages made from carved wood or cloth, china dolls from the Victorian age, knitted toys from World War II, metal Meccano sets from the 1950s through to the sophisticated electronic games of today.

- Find out what life was like for an employee in a Welsh copper mine, a Lancashire cotton mill or Cornish tin mine in the past.

Where do materials come from?

Draw and label the missing sections on this grid.

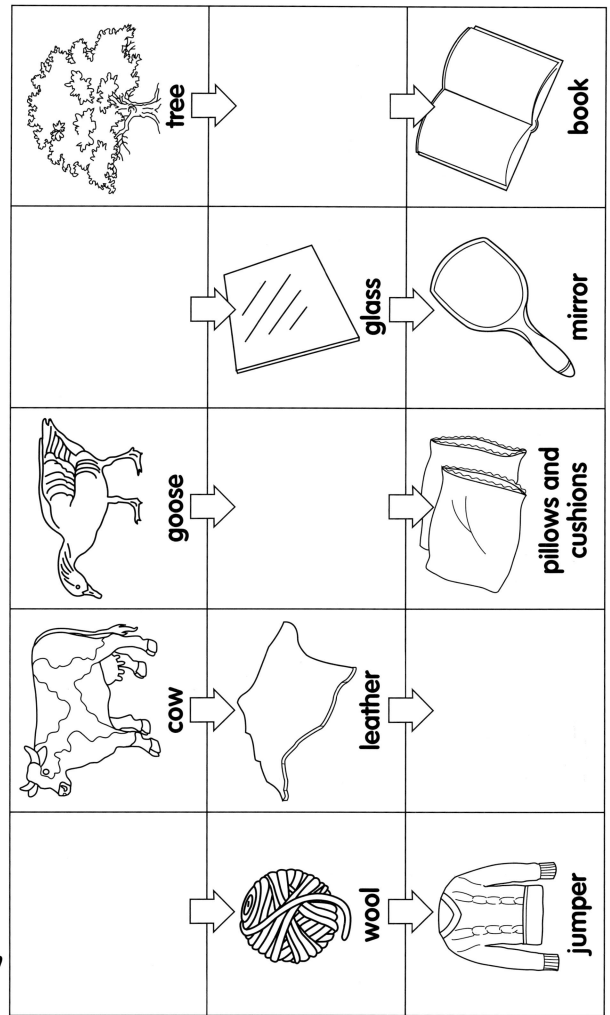

tree → → book

→ glass → mirror

goose → → pillows and cushions

cow → leather →

→ wool → jumper

Art

- Create masks from papier mâché and discuss the changes that occur to the paper throughout the process.

- Pour liquid plaster of Paris into a mould and leave to solidify. Take pictures of 'before and after' and discuss the changes.

- Create a mini sculpture by cutting a piece of sponge into a desired shape, then dip the sponge into plaster of Paris and leave to solidify. Paint and decorate the end product.

- Use clay or other mouldable materials to produce 3-D artefacts. Explore the property of clay before and after firing or drying.

- Use novelty ice moulds and coloured water to create a temporary ice sculpture.

- Create a collage using only naturally occurring materials such as feathers, bark or leaves. Discuss how the properties of some natural materials change, for example, flowers eventually wilt and die.

- Discuss images of sand or ice sculptures, identifying how the materials have been worked to produce an image.

Design & Technology

- Make fairy cakes following a simple recipe and note the change in state from the raw cake mixture to the cooked finished product.

- Melt some chocolate. Dip fresh fruit into the melted chocolate and leave in a cool place to allow the chocolate to solidify.

- Make a batch of bread dough. Ask the children to design and make a novelty loaf or roll, documenting the changes that occur as the raw dough rises whilst baking.

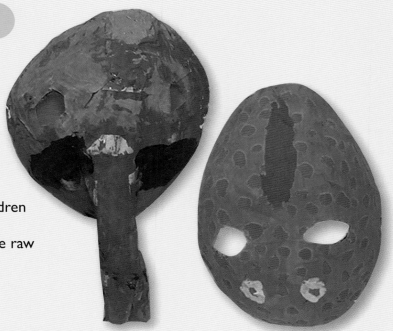

Grouping and Changing Materials

RE

- Discuss the word 'miracle' in religious stories and how this often relates to amazing changes. Explore miracles in a variety of religions. One example could be the story of the wedding in Cana from the Bible (John 2:1–11). This shows Jesus as a miracle maker, turning pots of water into wine. A display could be made about a chosen religious story.

- Investigate other miracles in Christianity and compare these with miracles in other faiths. There are many miracle stories involving the Hindu Gods. The explanation of how Ganesh got his elephant head is an example. This story can be found in *How Ganesh got his elephant head* by Harish Johari and Vatsala Sperling (Bear Cub Books). The following is also a useful source: *Hindu stories* by Anita Ganeri (Picture Window Books).

PSHCE

- Talk about recycling and how items can be re-used and changed into new packaging. Hold a recycling week in your class and attempt to recycle or re-use as many different classroom resources as possible.

- Buy and use a bin for recyclable paper waste in your classroom.

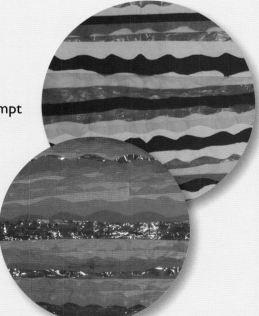

Music

- Sort and group instruments according to the material from which they have been made.

- Investigate the changes in the quality of sound that can be produced by striking the instruments in different places and in different ways.

Plants and Animals in the Local Area

These grids demonstrate the learning objectives covered in the activities within the theme. The curriculum references indicate the relevant programme of study (PoS) for a subject area unless otherwise stated.

	Learning Objectives	Curriculum References
Science (Page 54)		
Scientific Enquiry	Use close observation and first-hand experiences to explore minibeasts.	Sc1/2b
	Record and share findings.	Sc1/2f,g/ICT Pos 2a;3a
Life Processes and Living Things (QCA Science Unit 2B)	Understand that a wide variety of living things are present in the local environment. Understand that different livings things can be found in different habitats.	Sc2/5a,b
	Investigate plant and animal life, document and record findings.	Sc2/5a
	Obtain plant and animal images from the Internet.	ICT PoS 1a
	Use own criteria to sort livings things into groups.	Sc2/4b
	Consider the impact of human activity on local flora and fauna. Show care and concern for the environment.	Sc2/5c
	Create and use a database.	ICT PoS 1b,c
Literacy (Page 56)		
Listening and Responding	Ask and answer questions about a favourite animal character.	En1/2e
	Listen and respond to others.	En1/2c,d
Drama	Speak to others in the role of an animal from a story.	En1/11a
Engaging with and Responding to Texts	Read a range of fiction and non-fiction texts featuring animals.	En2/6a;7b
	Gather information about animals from texts.	En2/2a
Creating and Shaping Texts	Use a variety of stimuli for creative writing about animals.	En3/2c,d
	Use well-known stories as a starting point for own fiction.	En2/3f/En3/1f
Mathematics (Page 58)		
Using and Applying Mathematics	Solve open-ended number problems about animals through investigation.	Ma2/1a
	Choose and use appropriate operations. Check answers.	Ma2/1c,d;4a
Measuring	Use appropriate equipment to measure length and weight of pet animals.	Ma3/1b;4c
Handling Data	Collect information in a school bird survey.	Ma2/5a
	Use appropriate methods to record and sort information.	Ma2/5a
	Present information in a table or graphically.	Ma2/5a

Plants and Animals in the Local Area

Learning Objectives	Curriculum References
Design & Technology (Page 60)	
Use a variety of stimuli to generate ideas for an animal puppet.	QCA D&T Unit 2B PoS 1a-c/ ICT PoS 1a
Investigate ready-made animal puppets.	PoS 5a
Prepare materials, cut and sew a fabric puppet.	PoS 2c,d
Evaluate and use a finished product.	PoS 3a,b
PE (Page 60)	
Develop and perform animal movements and actions.	PoS 8a,b
Art (Page 62)	
Explore the different ways in which plants and animals have been represented through art.	QCA Art Unit 2B PoS 4c
Work collaboratively to create an animal wall hanging.	PoS 5b,c
Investigate colour mixing with paint to explore leaf colours.	PoS 2a;4a
PSHCE (Page 62)	
Find ways to improve and look after the school and local environments.	PoS 2g
Make positive choices about looking after plants and animals.	PoS 2c
RE (Page 62)	
Read and discuss creation stories (featuring animals and plants) from a range of religions and cultures.	PoS 1a;3a-c,f
Explore ways to celebrate the wonder of life on Earth.	PoS 1b;3g
History (Page 63)	
Investigate the lives of natural historians from the past.	QCA History Unit 4 PoS 6c
Show understanding of the different ways of life in the past.	PoS 2b
Geography (Page 63)	
Record 'green places' on a plan of the school.	PoS 2b
Use a map to locate specific land use and local habitats.	PoS 2c;4a
Understand how human activity can affect plants and animals.	PoS 5a
Identify ways in which the locality could be improved.	PoS 5b
Music (Page 63)	
Identify individual instruments in a piece of music.	PoS 4c
Use instruments to create specific sound effects to represent animals.	PoS 2b

Plants and Animals in the Local Area

Science

Starting Points

- Talk about which animals may be living in the local area. Look outside the school for evidence, such as paw prints or droppings, which indicate that mammals are in the area. The children should make a display showing pictures and facts about animals that would live in the locality.

Enquiry

- Focus attention onto the invertebrate life around the school. Ask the children to name any 'minibeasts' that they would expect to find in the area. Discuss how these could be observed and classified.

- Collect a large bucket of soil, dug up from the school grounds or a local garden. Empty the soil onto a large sheet of polythene on the classroom floor. Allow the children to search through the soil and collect minibeasts, placing them carefully onto a large tray for close observation. Hand lenses could be used for this purpose. A digital microscope could also be used to observe in even greater detail.

- Ask the children to keep a record of their findings, using an identification chart, such as the activity sheet on page 55. Encourage the children to record by drawing, with annotations, the creatures that they find. Remind the children to wash their hands thoroughly after the investigation and return the animals to the place that they originated from.

Extension

- Ask the children to suggest ways to sort the minibeasts that they have found in the soil, such as by their number of legs or the number of body parts. Find out how the minibeasts are classified in actuality. Does this resemble the way in which the children have classified the animals themselves?

- Certain mail order companies will send common British species of moth or butterfly eggs or caterpillars to schools. These can be kept in a 'moth tent' allowing children to observe how the caterpillars grow over time, create a chrysalis and, after a few weeks, emerge as a butterfly or moth. Provided that only British species are used, such as the Puss Moth, they can then be released in the local area.

Marvellous minibeasts

Many different minibeasts will be living in and around your school. Go on a minibeast hunt and see how many different creatures you can find.

Tick the boxes to show what you have found.

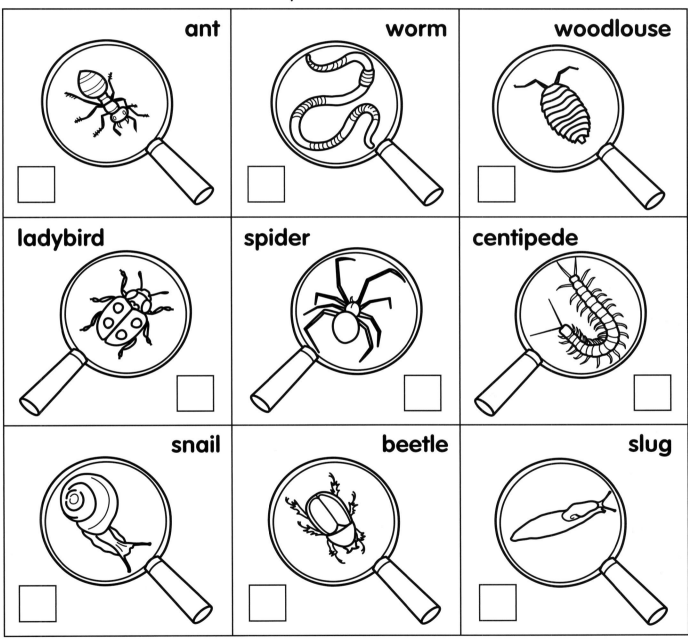

ant	worm	woodlouse
ladybird	spider	centipede
snail	beetle	slug

NOW! Make a careful, detailed drawing of one minibeast. Add labels to your drawing. Can you think of a way to classify minibeasts?

Remember to return your minibeasts to the place where you found them!

character descriptions

Literacy

Speaking and Listening

- Act out a well known animal story.

- Ask the children to imagine that they are going to interview a favourite animal character. They should write a list of questions using the activity sheet on page 57.

Reading and Writing

- Read a range of animal stories. Examples include: *Beatrix Potter: the complete tales* by Beatrix Potter (Frederick Warne), *The wind in the willows* by Kenneth Grahame (Wordsworth Children's Classics) and *Just so stories* by Rudyard Kipling (Pavilion Books). Read a selection of modern favourites such as *Frog is a hero* by Max Velthuijs (Andersen Press) and *Frog and Toad together* by Arnold Lobel (HarperCollins).

- Read non-fiction texts about plants and animals.

- Ask the children to write a birthday party invitation for a favourite animal story character.

- The children could write a new, alternative ending for a well known animal story.

- Research and write a factsheet about an endangered species of plant or animal.

- There is life on Mars! Ask the children to pretend they have found a new plant or animal on planet Mars. They have the honour of naming this new species. They should draw and label it and write a description of their amazing find.

- Cut out images of animals from magazines. Choose two or more images and write out the conversation that the animals are having, using speech bubbles.

- Make a list of well known animal story characters, then sort the animals into groups according to characteristics such as 'sly', 'helpful' and 'clever'. A display should be compiled with drawings of the characters surrounded by sentences describing them.

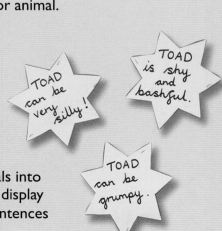

Plants and Animals in the Local Area

ANIMALS IN STORIES

Imagine that you are going to interview an animal character from a story. Think about what happens in the story and write down the questions you would like to ask.

The story I have chosen is:	The animal I would like to interview is:

Who_____

_____?

Where_____

_____?

Why_____

_____?

When _____

_____?

How_____

_____?

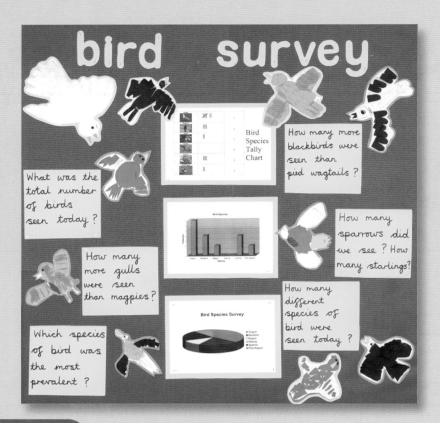

Maths

Using and Applying

● Carry out an open-ended number investigation based on the number of legs of animals. For example, how many different ways can a total of 18 or 24 legs be made using different combinations of animals? For example, a woodlouse (14 legs) plus honey bee (six legs) plus fox (four legs) makes a total of 24 legs. Use a pictorial grid of animals to select from.

Measuring

● Investigate measurements of a mammal, such as a rabbit. Use scales to weigh the animal. Use a tape measure to measure the length of its body, ears, feet and whiskers. Record findings using standard units of measurement.

● Draw around a variety of different leaves. Use string to find out the measurement of the perimeter of each leaf. Draw around leaves on squared paper to introduce the idea of surface area.

Handling Data

● Organise teams of children to watch for birds in the school grounds. They should use a tally chart to record observations and then use the data to create a graph. Ask and answer questions about the data. Make a display of the survey results.

● The children could complete the activity sheet on page 59, answering questions relating to data shown on a bar chart.

● Use sorting hoops or a Carroll diagram to sort leaves according to given criteria, such as long leaves/round leaves, smooth leaves/hairy leaves.

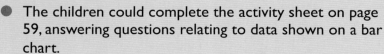

BIRD SURVEY

The children in class 2C at Priory Fields School completed a bird survey. Their results are presented here as a bar chart.

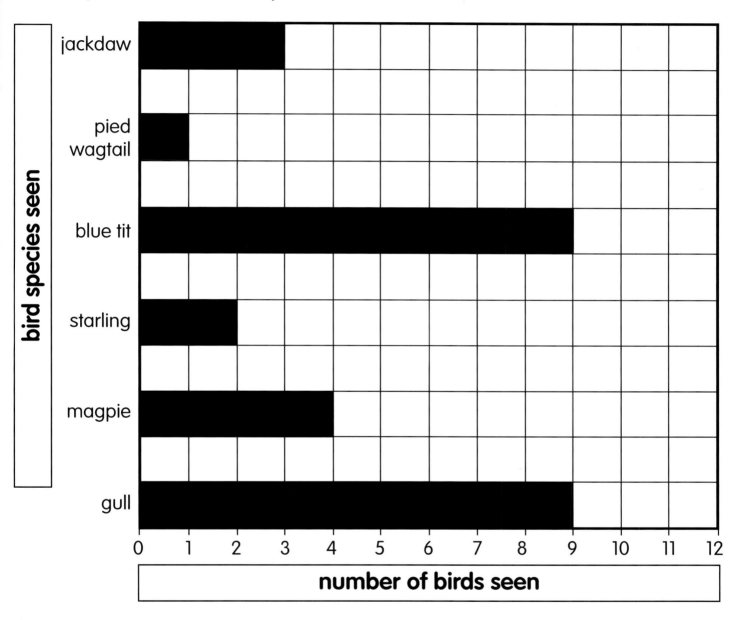

- How many gulls were seen?
- How many more magpies were seen than starlings?
- The same number of birds were seen for which two species?
- How many starlings and wagtails were seen?
- What was the total number of birds seen in the survey?

 **Make a tally chart of these results.**

• Plants and Animals in the Local Area • Belair Curricular-Links Science 2

Design & Technology

● Make a class collection of animal hand puppets. Examine what they have been made from, how they have been assembled and how they have been decorated or embellished. Look at images of British wildlife from reference books or from Internet websites. Referring to the puppet collection and the pictures viewed, the children should now design their own animal hand puppet.

– Children should make a paper pattern for the puppet by drawing around their hand as a starting point. Remind them to make the pattern big enough to allow a hand to go into the puppet and leave sufficient room for the stitched edge.

– Attach the paper pattern to two pieces of fabric with pins and cut around the pattern. Then remove the pattern, pin the two pieces of fabric back together and stitch around the edge of the puppet.

– Decorate the puppet using a glue-gun to attach fabric pieces, or sew on items such as buttons or sequins.

– Ask the children to evaluate the finished puppet against their original design drawing. (The activity sheet on page 61 could be completed at this point.) They should consider if the puppet met the design intention and discuss ways in which their puppet could be improved.

PE

● Play an animal movement game. Ask the children to name some local wildlife and then create a movement for each animal, such as scurrying like a mouse, hopping like a rabbit, or leaping like a hare. Call out an animal and the children must travel around the hall space, using the agreed gestures and movements for that animal. Use a call of 'Hibernate!' or 'Children coming!' to stop the action.

Plants and Animals in the Local Area

MY PUPPET

Draw a picture of your finished puppet here.

List the things you used to make your puppet.

-
-
-
-
-
-
-
-
-
-

Write three things that you really like about your puppet.

 1. _____

 2. _____

 3. _____

Write down one thing that could make your puppet even better.

_____

NOW! **Use your puppet to act out a story with your friends.**

Art

- Create an animal-themed, decorative wall hanging. Provide children with an animal outline on fabric, such as felt, to cut out and decorate. Ask the children to stitch the decorated animals onto a square of fabric, such as calico. Assemble the calico squares onto a large piece of fabric, such as a single bed-sheet, and use a sewing machine to stitch on the squares.

- Create a natural colour chart using leaves. Look at green paint colour charts from a DIY store as a starting point then create a natural colour chart using a selection of leaves collected from around the school. Attach the leaves with glue or tape to paper, using the gradients of the colour green in the different leaves to create a colour sequence. Using colour-mixing, create matching colours from paint and apply the colour next to each leaf.

PSHCE

- Ask the children to each become a 'garden guardian'. Explain that this entails a duty of care to the living things around them. Agree upon a charter and ask the children to sign up to it.

- Have a 'garden guardian' activity day. This could include creating a new habitat for wildlife, such as creating a new log pile for invertebrates, clearing up litter from a neglected area, caring for the pond area by removing unwanted plant material, planting seeds or bulbs in the school garden or installing bird and bat boxes.

- Investigate the Countryside Code. Look at the advice given on www.countryside.gov.uk

RE

- Read the Christian story of St Francis of Assisi to the children and talk about how and why he devoted his life to the care of animals. Published stories include, *The good man of Assisi* by Mary Joslin (Lion Hudson) or *Who was St Francis of Assisi?* by Lucy Lethbridge (Short Books).

- Read animal stories from *Animal tales: favourite stories from the Bible* by Nick Butterworth (Candle Books).

- Talk about creation stories from different faiths and cultures, such as the Australian Aboriginal and North American Indian creation stories.

History

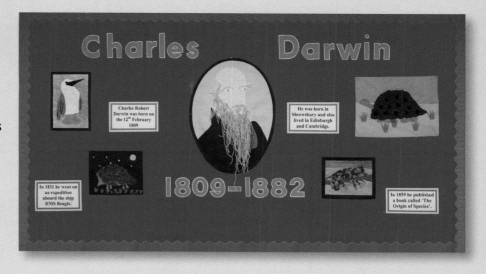

- Find out information about famous natural historians such as Charles Darwin (1809–1882) or Joseph Banks (1743–1820). Create a class display about the life and times of this person.

- Create a chronological timeline display in the classroom about the chosen famous figure.

- Ask the children to imagine they are a Victorian botanist on an exploration in a tropical jungle, who has just found an amazing new species of flowering plant! Ask them to write a journal page with all the details of their discovery. Include a description of the plant and its location, what they will name the plant and how they plan to get it back to the curator of Kew Gardens in London in one piece!

- Carry out a research project on how plants and animals have been used across the ages. The children could focus their investigation on one area, such as on the domestication of animals or on the cultivation of crops.

Geography

- Use a map of the local area to identify where 'green places' can be found in your locality, such as parks, woodlands, marshes and wetlands, fields and farms. Ask the children to describe where the places are and find out which children have visited or made use of these green places. Encourage the children to discuss their views about the local environment.

- Ask the children to speculate which animals, such as British mammals, may be living in the local area. Ask the children to consider the local area as a habitat for wildlife and what could be done to encourage more wildlife into the area.

- Ask the children to consider what impact, if any, that human development, such as new housing or a road widening scheme, may have on the plants and animals in the locality.

- Ask a volunteer from the local wildlife trust to come in and talk to the children about the local flora and fauna. You may have specialised species in your own backyard! According to the specific geography of your area, these could include species of orchids or ferns, butterflies or birds. Focus on how aspects of localised human and physical features influence the type of and abundance of plant and animal species.

Music

- Listen to a recording of *The carnival of animals* by Camille Saint-Saëns (1835–1921) and discuss how the tempo and type of instrument have been used to capture the essence of an animal.

- Use the work of Saint-Saëns as a starting point for the children's own composition about an animal, perhaps a class pet or an animal that has been spotted in the school grounds.

Plants and Animals in the Local Area

Variation

These grids demonstrate the learning objectives covered in the activities within the theme. The curriculum references indicate the relevant programme of study (PoS) for a subject area unless otherwise stated.

	Learning Objectives	Curriculum References
Science (Page 66)		
Scientific Enquiry	Collect evidence about classification through direct handling and observation of pets.	Sc1/2b
	Make measurements, drawings and notes.	Sc1/2f
	Make comparisons between living things.	Sc1/2h
Life Processes and Living Things (QCA Science Unit 2C)	Handle animals with care.	Sc2/2e
	Identify ways in which people are the same and different.	Sc2/4a
	Group animals according to similarities and differences.	Sc2/4b
Literacy (Page 68)		
Drama	Act out a story about 'differences' to others.	En1/4b;11b
Understanding and Interpreting Texts	Read stories that celebrate 'differences' and talk about the things that happen and why.	En2/1m;3b
Creating and Shaping Texts	Use stories as a starting point for own work.	En3/1f
	Plan and write stories and non-fiction accounts about classification.	En3/2c,d
Mathematics (Page 70)		
Using and Applying Mathematics	Solve addition problems related to variation.	Ma2/3a
	Investigate a line of enquiry choosing appropriate operations.	Ma2/1a,c
Measuring	Use standards units of measurement.	Ma3/4a
	Measure length of shoe size, hands and other variables.	Ma3/4c
Handling Data	Collect information to answer questions about variation in length and height.	Ma2/1a
	Use tables and diagrams to sort information about living things.	Ma2/5a,b

Learning Objectives	Curriculum References
PSHCE (Page 72)	
Identify positive aspects about oneself and others.	PoS 1d;5b
Recognise similarities and differences between people.	PoS 4c
Show respect for others.	PoS 4c

Learning Objectives	Curriculum References
RE (Page 72)	
Explore the use of songs and hymns in worship and praise.	PoS 1b,d;3a-c,g,l,o
Consider ways in which life on Earth may be represented and celebrated.	PoS 1b,d;3a-d,g
Music (Page 72)	
Sing songs about plants and animals.	PoS 1a
Consider musical elements such as timbre.	PoS 4b
Compose, create and perform music with a plant or animal theme.	PoS 1b,1c;2b
Art (Page 74)	
Use natural objects as a starting point for work.	PoS 5a
Explore the use of tools and techniques including printing and collage.	PoS 2a/b/5c
Examine natural colours using items such as leaves and petals.	PoS 4a
Look at portraits by famous artists.	PoS 4c
Design & Technology (Page 74)	
Look at animal fabrics and prints to generate initial ideas.	PoS 1a
Rehearse the skill of tightly rolling paper.	PoS 5a
Assemble materials to create a product, such as a necklace.	PoS 2d
History (Page 75)	
Study the life and work of Carl Linnaeus.	PoS 6c
Use sources of information including books, newspapers and the Internet to find out about variation.	PoS 4a/ICT PoS 1a
Geography (Page 75)	
Locate and compare plants and animals in countries on a map or globe.	PoS 2c
Describe what places are like in terms of animal habitats.	PoS 3a
Research information from the Internet.	PoS 2d/ICT PoS 1a

Variation

Starting Points

- Make a visit to a zoo, botanical garden or arboretum. Use the 'clever classifying' activity sheet on page 67 as an introduction to classifying.

- Ask the children to focus on the reasons why certain animals are classified together. Discuss observable similarities within the group and the differences that can be seen when comparing two or more different groups. Find out about the classification system and start a large wall display to illustrate this.

Enquiry

- Bring into the classroom two familiar pet animals, such as a rabbit and a guinea pig. Parental consent must be given prior to this activity, as children may have an allergic reaction to animal fur and there is also the risk of a child receiving a scratch or bite.

  – Remind the children that living things must be treated with care. Explain to them that the animals are both mammals and that they both belong to the same group of mammals, called rodents.

  – Allow the children to observe at close-hand and if, possible, gently handle the animals in order to discern observable similarities and differences. Ask the children to consider other aspects about the animals, such as type of diet.

- Draw the animals, adding labels and annotations to highlight features that they have taken note of. Ask the children to feed back to the class the things that are the same about the animals, and also the things that make the two animals different. Then, imagine if a non-rodent pet, such as a cat, bird or snake were to have been brought into the classroom. *What would be the observable differences between these animals and the pet rodents that featured in the investigation today?*

Extension Activities

- Show the children images, perhaps as a PowerPoint® presentation, of a bat, a human and a whale. Remark on how incredibly different these animals are when compared against each other. Now remind the children that these three animals are all examples of mammals and are, as such, classified in the same group together. Ask, *How can this be?* In order to all belong to the same group these animals must share common features and attributes. Challenge the children to discover what these common characteristics are. Ask, *What makes a mammal a mammal?*

Clever classifying

Cut out these pictures and sort them into the following groups:

fish · insect · amphibian · bird · reptile · mammal

frog

salmon

bee

dolphin

tortoise

human

snake

mackerel

starling

butterfly

bat

newt

seal

robin

crocodile

NOW!

Choose one group of animals and write down three reasons why the animals in the group belong together.

• Variation • Belair Curricular-Links Science 2

Literacy

Speaking and Listening

● Invite a local gardener, grocer or farmer to come into the class and talk about the different varieties of locally grown produce, for instance the different varieties of apple grown in an orchard or the different varieties of potato crop.

Reading and Writing

● Read and use non-fiction texts, such as *Animal classification* by Polly Goodman (Hodder Wayland) or books from the *Variety of life* series written by Joy Richardson (Franklin Watts).

● Read and discuss the story *Ruby* by Maggie Glen (Red Fox). Ask the children to re-tell the story in their own words. Discuss why Ruby is initially rejected and how she finally finds a loving home. The children could then plan and write a similar story, where a dramatic climax involving rejection is resolved in a positive ending.

　– Ask the children to complete a reading comprehension activity, using the worksheet provided on page 69. When asking verbal questions to the children encourage them to provide evidence, by referring back to the text, to substantiate their answers.

　– Ask the children to write a book review for this story. These could be displayed in the classroom.

● Organise the children into groups and ask them to collaboratively write a short play script about a playground situation in which someone is rejected because they are different. Encourage a positive resolution to the story. Ask each group to act out their play to the rest of the class.

● Ask the children to write a factual account highlighting variation within a group of animals. Focus on a familiar subject such as dogs and the children could then write about the different breeds, from Great Dane to Chihuahua! Pieces written by individual children could be collated to produce a whole-class big book.

Reading about Ruby

Read *Ruby* by Maggie Glen. Now, answer the following questions.

What was Mrs Harris daydreaming about while she was making Ruby in the factory?

Tick **two** things that were different about Ruby.

feet ☐   fur ☐

ears ☐   tail ☐

claws ☐   nose ☐

Match the beginning of each sentence with its correct ending.

● Ruby was   took the bus home.

● The big bear   thrown in a box.

● The workers   started snoring.

Which **two** words describe how the bears ran away from the factory?

_____

Susie has a necklace with a silver letter 's' hanging on it.
What does Ruby think the letter stands for?

_____

Write a short book review about the story.

Maths

Using and Applying

- Investigate a line of enquiry relating to the variation in measurement of children in the class, such as 'Is it true that the tallest children also have the largest feet?'

- Ask the children to classify themselves into groups according to age. Find out how many children are of which age in the class. Ask each child to calculate how many birthday cake candles they themselves have had. For instance, a child of six would have had 1 + 2 + 3 + 4 + 5 + 6 = 21 candles in their lifetime. Challenge the children to find out the collective total of birthday cake candles for a seven- or eight-year-old.

Measuring

- Investigate the variation in the size of the children in the class by measuring variables such as shoe size, height, weight and handspan.

Handling Data

- Ask the children to sort and organise information about the characteristics of people in the class. Use the 'sorting information' activity sheet on page 71 as a starting point.

- Encourage use of different criteria with which to sort children. You could sort using two large hoops to create a Venn diagram or use a Carroll diagram as illustrated on the activity sheet. Talk about the data collected and pose questions, such as, *How many people are over one metre in height? What is the range of handspan measurement in the class? How many more people are shoe size 2 than size 1?*

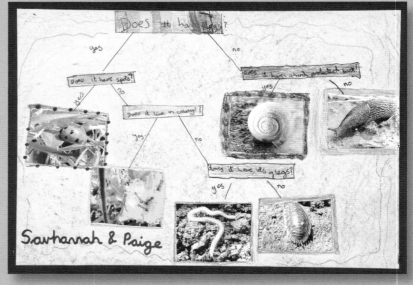

- Use information about the variety of minibeasts found in the school grounds, for example, to create 'branching tree' databases as shown on the display. Present the data appropriately in a chart or table. Children could use the data to produce a pictogram or discrete data graph.

- Ask the children to suggest ways in which all the teachers in the school could be classified and sorted.

Variation

Sorting information

BETH

SAM

CASEY

JADE

RAJESH

ANITA

TIFFANY

BRANDON

Write the children's names in the correct position on this Carroll diagram.

	black hair	not black hair
glasses		
no glasses		

Sort the data again using your own criteria.

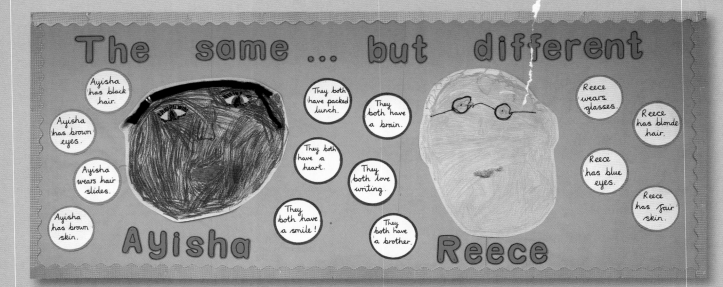

PSHCE

● Using a collection of 'people' dolls or figures, ask the children to select two figures each and, working with a partner, discuss the ways in which the figures selected are the same and ways in which they are different. Talk about the importance of respecting differences between people.

● Ask each child to select a member of the class to draw and write about, focusing on similarities and differences between themselves. The activity sheet on page 73 should be used for this activity. Display the pictures together with captions stating how people are the same and different.

● Ask the children to identify an aspect about themselves which makes them special and unique. This could become the basis of a display designed to encourage inspiration and aspiration.

RE

● Sing the well known Christian hymn *All things bright and beautiful*. Talk about the message in the hymn. Ask the children to write a new verse for this hymn, perhaps focusing on a specific animal or plant.

● Create a 3-D display of Noah's Ark, using rolled-up newspapers as a framework for the bodies and limbs of animals. Once a framework has been made, papier mâché can be applied to create features. The models can be painted appropriately.

Music

● Listen to and sing songs about animal and plant life. Use as a starting point for creating a class song about the variety of life.

● Ask the children to create music for a 'parade of plants'. Talk about which plants they will include in the musical parade. Generate ideas for how they are going to use instruments to represent rustling leaves, tremendous tree trunks, soft and spongy moss, unfurling ferns, delicate blossoms, swaying seaweed and so on.

The same ... but different

 Draw a picture of yourself and a picture of a friend.

ME

MY FRIEND

How are you the same?
Write four points.

-
-
-
-

How are you different?
Write four points.

-
-
-
-

NOW! List the things that you and your friend like doing together.

Art

- Collect images of animals from magazines. Create a display: using a leaf-shaped template, cut out the animals to create leaves for a 'tree of life' collage.

- Look at the variety of natural patterns found on animals, such as the stripes on a zebra and a tiger, the patches of colour on a giraffe and the spots on a leopard. Use everyday items including junk box materials as printing tools and recreate animal print patterns on paper or fabric using paint and printing techniques.

- Flowers come in a huge variety of colours. Make and display a large floral colour wheel, using images of flowers to make up coloured segments. The colour collection could include: red poppies and roses, yellow primroses, sunflowers and daffodils, orange marigolds, blue hyacinths and purple irises.

- Collect a selection of natural objects from around the school grounds, such as leaves in varying shades, petals, twigs and seeds. Use them to create a textured, natural collage.

- Look at a selection of famous portraits and talk about how the artists have used colour, light and texture to create effects and the many different ways in which the human face has been captured and represented through art.

Design & Technology

- Draw and annotate designs for a new greenhouse (such as those at Kew Gardens in London). Think about what the structure of the building will look like and its internal layout. Ask, *Which plants will you include in your collection? What information will you display to the public and how will this be arranged?*

- Using the colours and patterns from the animal world as a starting point, design and make items of 'wildlife' jewellery. Beads made from rolled-up strips of paper could be painted with black and white zebra stripes and strung together as a necklace. Painted pasta pieces could be glued to card to form a brooch.

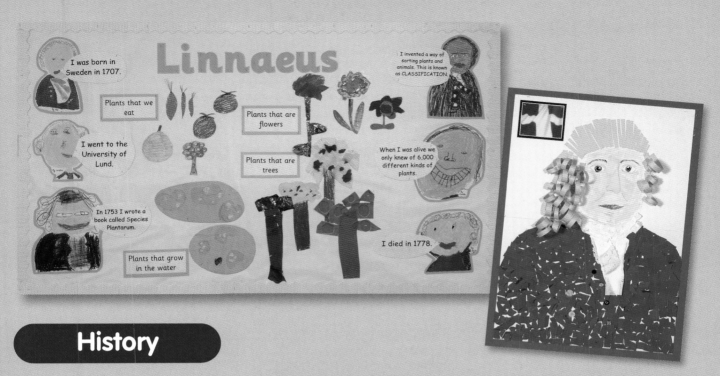

History

- Research the life of Carl Linnaeus (1707–1778), the Swedish scientist who pioneered the use of the classification system still in use today. Search for images of Linnaeus on the Internet. The children should draw pictures of Linnaeus and items relating to him. Use these pictures to create a display about Linnaeus, also featuring important facts about his life and work.

- Find out about common reactions at the time to the work of Charles Darwin (1809–1882), in particular the reaction of many Victorians to his assertion that humans have evolved from the same common ancestor as apes and are therefore closely related to them. Look at newspaper articles and cartoons from the period. Talk about why people reacted in this way.

- Read *Gregor Mendel: The friar who grew peas* by Cheryl Bardoe (Harry N. Abrams) as a starting point for a project on the life and work of Gregor Mendel (1822–1884) who, in the nineteenth century, investigated variation and heredity in plants.

Geography

- Choose a place that is geographically isolated from the rest of the world. Islands such as Australia or Madagascar would be two suitable examples. Look at the variation in plant and animal life that has occurred in such places. Livings things have evolved here separately from the rest of the world over millennia, resulting in specialised indigenous species, which cannot be found anywhere else on Earth. Australian marsupials or Madagascan lemurs, for instance, are two groups of animals worthy of investigating.

- Look at a list of animals considered to be in grave danger of extinction. Locate the places where these animals can be found. Ask the children to suggest the reasons for the terminal decline of these animals. Visiting the EDGE (Evolutionary Distinct and Globally Endangered) website at www.edgeofexistence.org is a good place to start.

- Focus on one family of animals and find out about the variation that occurs within this family across the globe. The cat family, for instance, would make an interesting study. Places where cat species are found could be identified on a map of the world and comparisons made between the animals – Scottish wild cat, European lynx, African lion, Asian tiger and snow leopards in the Himalayas are just a few examples.

Assessment Ideas

In any activity the children carry out, whether through discussing, planning, doing or writing, there is an element of assessment. There are many ways to assess children – see the ideas below and the grid on page 77 for further suggestions. Knowledge-based assessments should use a variety of methods such as games, quizzes, drama and role play presentations, discussion of 'concept cartoons' and completing 'concept maps'.

- Concept cartoons are a useful tool in teaching and assessing. Each cartoon takes an everyday scientific idea about which three or more points of view are shown. For example, it could be a variety of views about how quickly objects fall. The cartoons encourage children to think carefully about what is being discussed and say which point of view they agree with and why. The cartoons generally portray a range of ideas which can be used to promote discussion of the children's own ideas and inform teachers what to teach and how to group children. For more information visit www.conceptcartoons.com

- Concept maps are also useful. The idea is to link nouns about a theme with arrows. The arrow shows the connection between the two words. For example:

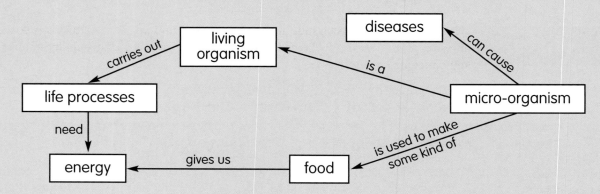

- Ensure that you have clear learning objectives for your lessons and that these are shared and understood by the children.

- Tell the children what the success criteria are and how they can achieve them.

- When marking children's work, highlight successes against the learning objective and write affirmative statements on the page, such as 'you can make a circuit' or 'you can name parts of the body'.

- Include time for assessment work in your daily and weekly planning. You may wish to conduct an end of topic investigation to access the children's level of knowledge and understanding.

- At the end of the topic, create a spreadsheet document to record the children's attainment against the objectives. Colour-code the cells: red for not achieved, orange for objective met and green for those who have exceeded expectations. This will produce an 'at a glance' reference to achievement and will highlight areas that need further work. Such documents could be handed on with other record-keeping to inform planning in subsequent year groups.

- Self-assessment sheets for children to complete are included on pages 78–80. The sheets cover areas of knowledge taught throughout the year. Children should be given their own sheets at the end of teaching a theme for them to colour in the objectives achieved. These could be colour-coded for those areas they think they know well/are uncertain about/do not know. The 'I can …' statements of skills will be practised in different contexts throughout the year, so children need to make judgements on each one more than once, again at the end of each theme and they should write the date in the column when the skill is achieved. Use all the sheets alongside your assessments to inform reports and general assessment at the end of the school year.

Who Should Assess?

Anyone involved with children's learning can assess, including parents and the children themselves. The most important thing is that the assessor knows what they are looking for and has the skills and knowledge to make these judgements. Children can assess each other – but they should always try to be constructive – what are the good points as well as the not so good?

HOW	TIPS
Observation of Children Working	Use this method when there is no written work as evidence, for example when children are planning and discussing. Assess a single child or a group by questioning the children to clarify understanding.
Group Feedback	Use this method to clarify the understanding of 'quiet' children, or those you are unsure about. Allow the 'listening' children to ask questions of 'presenters'. Ask questions of the children to gain a greater understanding of their learning.
Recording Children's Views During an Activity	Gather the children's opinions and ideas during activities. Ask the children to make their own recordings for you to listen to after the lesson.
Drama	This method is fun and non-threatening for children as they can 'show' instead of writing their understanding of key objectives. Use role play to discuss issues and act out events and imaginary situations such as, 'inside a part of the body', 'in space' or 'inside the Earth' to clarify understanding of key concepts.
Concept Cartoons	Use at the beginning and/or at the end of lessons to clarify children's ideas.
Diagrams, Drawings and Photographs	Ask the children to draw ideas before teaching and at the end to compare understanding of concepts. Make/interpret concept maps before and after lessons/topics. Photograph the children's work before/after the topic is complete to compare.
Sort a Collection	Ask the children to sort a collection of objects/vocabulary related to the topic in different ways. This method is particularly good for maths and science, to pinpoint the children's grasp of skills and knowledge.
Make & Play a Game	Incorporate key concepts and vocabulary into games, for example create questions that the children have to answer correctly before they move a space on a board game. Laminate games and retain for future use.
Devise & Answer Questions	Put questions in a box (generated by the teacher and the children) and ask the children to answer them over the course of the topic.
Interactive Display	Put questions on displays which highlight key concepts instead of labels. Add to the display as the topic progresses.
Types of Quiz	Create a true/false quiz on areas of knowledge and play this before and after teaching the topic to compare the children's responses. Quizzes can be oral or written by the children or teacher.
Written Work	Writing is useful as evidence but be aware that this is not always the best way for children to demonstrate what they know or can do. Use different genres of writing.

Assessment Ideas

Life Processes and Living Things

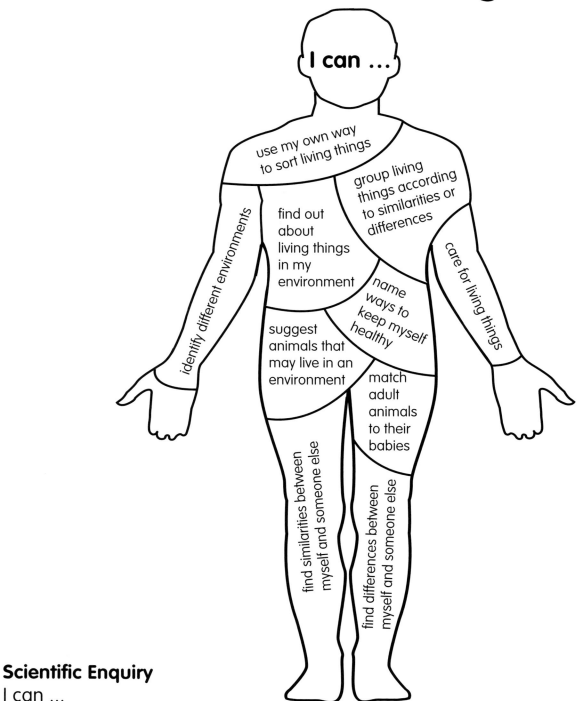

I can ...

- use my own way to sort living things
- group living things according to similarities or differences
- find out about living things in my environment
- identify different environments
- care for living things
- name ways to keep myself healthy
- suggest animals that may live in an environment
- match adult animals to their babies
- find similarities between myself and someone else
- find differences between myself and someone else

Scientific Enquiry

I can ...

Skill	Date	Date	Date	Skill	Date	Date	Date
listen to and follow instructions				share ideas with others			
ask questions about things around me				collect evidence through observation			
talk about ways to answer questions				use equipment to make measurements			
use scientific language to describe and explain things				draw pictures with labels and captions			
suggest different ways to find information				talk with others about what has been found			

Materials and their Properties

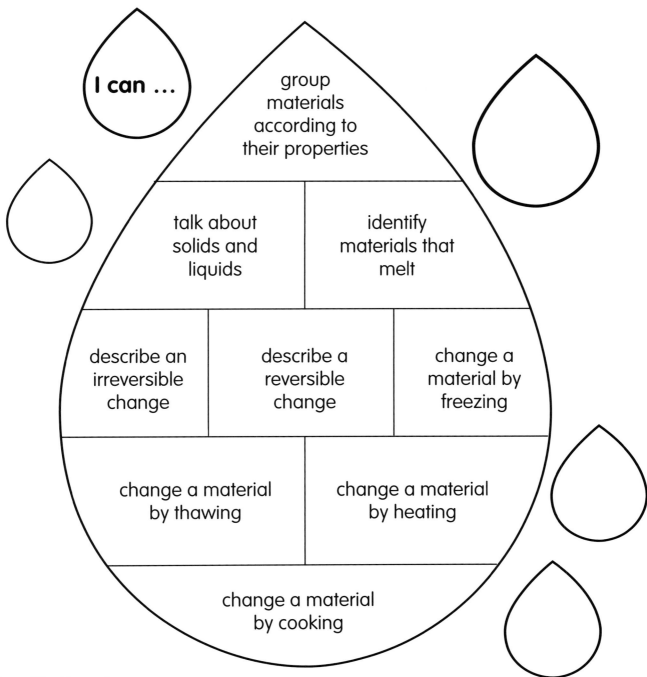

I can ...

group materials according to their properties

talk about solids and liquids

identify materials that melt

describe an irreversible change

describe a reversible change

change a material by freezing

change a material by thawing

change a material by heating

change a material by cooking

Scientific Enquiry

I can ...

Skill	Date	Date	Date	Skill	Date	Date	Date
ask questions about things around me				talk about how to keep a test fair			
talk about ways to answer questions				make a prediction			
share ideas with others				make and record observations			
use scientific language to describe and explain things				explain to others what has happened			

Physical Processes

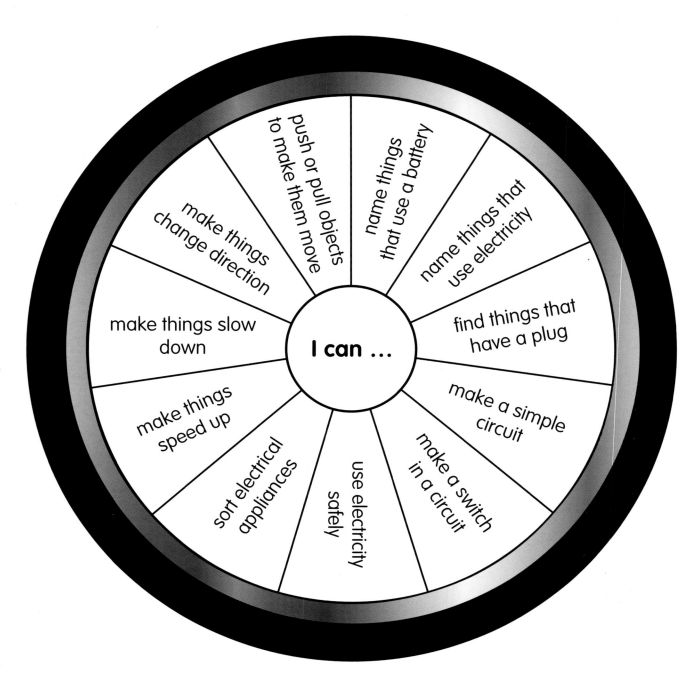

In the wheel, around "I can ...":
- push or pull objects to make them move
- name things that use a battery
- name things that use electricity
- find things that have a plug
- make a simple circuit
- make a switch in a circuit
- use electricity safely
- sort electrical appliances
- make things speed up
- make things slow down
- make things change direction

Scientific Enquiry

I can ...

Skill	Date	Date	Date	Skill	Date	Date	Date
share ideas with others				select the equipment I will need			
ask questions about things around me				use equipment safely			
investigate by trying things out for myself				make and record observations			
talk about what I expect will happen				present and explain findings to others			